CONCORDIA UNIVERSITY

QP601.F361964
STRUCTURE AND ACTIVITY OF ENZYMES

D1382678

WITHDRAWN

DATE DUE

NO2 9'95			

DEMCO 38-297

STRUCTURE AND ACTIVITY

OF ENZYMES

FEDERATION OF EUROPEAN BIOCHEMICAL SOCIETIES
SYMPOSIUM NO. 1 HELD IN LONDON ON 24TH MARCH 1964

Edited by

T. W. GOODWIN
J. I. HARRIS
B. S. HARTLEY

 1964

ACADEMIC PRESS • London and New York

KLINCK MEMORIAL LIBRARY
Concordia Teachers College
River Forest, Illinois

ACADEMIC PRESS INC. (LONDON) LTD
Berkeley Square House
Berkeley Square
London, W.1.

U.S. Edition published by

ACADEMIC PRESS INC.
111 Fifth Avenue
New York, New York 10003

Copyright © 1964 by the Federation of European Biochemical Societies
Second printing 1965

Library of Congress Catalog Card Number: 64–66135

Printed in Great Britain by
The Whitefriars Press Ltd.,
London and Tonbridge.

79822

PREFACE

The Federation of European Biochemical Societies came into being on 1 January 1964. It was planned at a meeting of delegates of 17 European Biochemical Societies, held in Oxford in July 1963. All the Societies subsequently agreed to join the Federation and the number has grown to 19, representing Austria, Belgium, Bulgaria, Czechoslovakia, Denmark, Finland, France, Germany, Great Britain, Hungary, Italy, The Netherlands, Norway, Poland, Spain, Sweden, and Switzerland.

Membership of the Federation is conferred automatically on members of each constituent Society. The Federation exists to promote closer co-operation between biochemists in Europe, among other things by holding annual meetings. The symposium printed here took place on 24 March 1964, during the first Federation Meeting on 23–25 March 1964 in London. The Biochemical Society of Great Britain, which organized the first meeting for the Federation, is grateful to Dr. F. Sanger and Professor T. W. Goodwin who arranged the symposium, to Drs. B. S. Hartley and J. I. Harris for editing the manuscripts, to the Royal Society and the Wellcome Trust for financial assistance to the speakers and, foremost, to the speakers themselves.

The Federation has a brief, informal list of Statutes. It does not propose to have a permanent secretariat. The administration changes as each Society in turn holds a Federation Meeting. In its short existence the Federation has already promoted much closer relations between European biochemists and practical benefits have emerged. For example, over 500 biochemists took part in Federation air charters from London and Paris to the Sixth International Congress of Biochemistry in New York in July 1964. The Federation has planned summer schools for training in advanced research methods and "Gordon-style" research conferences are envisaged for the future. This symposium is the first in a series which will emanate from the annual meetings.

As the first officers of the Federation, appointed by The Biochemical Society, we have been delighted by the success of the first year's activities and grateful for the support of all the adhering Societies. The fact that European scientists in other disciplines are now planning co-operative ventures modelled on that of the biochemists is a welcome compliment.

F. C. Happold *Chairman*
W. J. Whelan *Secretary*
S. P. Datta *Treasurer*

CONTENTS

HAEMOGLOBIN

Morning Session

Chairman : P. Desnuelle

Introduction by F. Sanger†

The chemical processes of living matter are almost entirely dependent on the catalytic activity of enzymes, so that the problems of what enzymes are and how they work are two of the most fundamental in biochemistry. It is clear that this activity must depend on the exact chemical structure of the molecule and particularly on the nature of that part of the enzyme that comes into contact with the substrate and is generally referred to as the "active site". In the past, many studies have used indirect approaches to deduce something of the nature of active sites, but these have been greatly hampered by a lack of the knowledge of the chemical structure of the enzymes involved. During recent years there has been considerable progress in studies of protein structure, both in the determination of amino acid sequences by chemical methods and in the elucidation of the configuration by the X-ray method, so that we are rapidly approaching a situation where it will be possible to give the exact chemical structure of an enzyme and probably to explain the details of its catalytic mechanism. This is the subject of the present symposium. The problem will be dealt with mainly from the point of view of the protein chemist; however, there are many other aspects of enzymology that must be considered in any attempt to understand enzymes.

Because of the great amount of work that is going on in this subject, it is only possible to deal with a few special topics. We have chosen to deal with three proteins about which much is known from the chemical point of view, and to have a special section on the new methods for specifically labelling active sites. The inclusion of haemoglobin in a symposium on enzymes seems justified since much is known about its active site, and a consideration of its structure and activity is likely to teach us much about enzymes.

† Read in his absence by P. Desnuelle

1

RIBONUCLEASE

Structure and Activity of Ribonuclease

F. M. RICHARDS

Department of Molecular Biology and Biophysics,
Yale University, New Haven, Connecticut, U.S.A.

Since the first report of its purification by Kunitz (1940), ribonuclease isolated from bovine pancreas has been the subject of a rapidly increasing number of studies in the field of protein chemistry. The great stability and low molecular weight have been important factors in the frequent choice of the enzyme. As a macromolecule, ribonuclease now occupies the position of a primary standard for the calibration of many physical and chemical techniques. However, its mechanism of action as an enzyme is still unknown. Some aspects of the chemistry of this protein are discussed in this paper.

The initial studies of Anfinsen and the work of Hirs, Stein and Moore and their colleagues have provided the entire covalent structure of this molecule (see Figure 1). Knowledge of the sequence has encouraged the detailed study of the chemical modification of a number of functional groups. In the case of limited reaction, the modified residues can usually be definitively located in any part of the sequence. A number of such residues whose covalent structure has been modified by the addition or substitution of one or more atoms are shown in the circles in Figure 1.

CHEMICAL MODIFICATION OF RIBONUCLEASE-A

Hirs (1962) has made a detailed study of the reaction between 1-fluoro-2,4-dinitrobenzene (FDNB) and RNase-A. The principal products of the initial stages are mono-DNP derivatives of the α-amino group of residue 1 and the ε-amino group of residue 41. The former derivative has partial enzymic activity, the latter is inactive. The reactivity of the group at position 41 is almost two orders of magnitude greater than that of a similar amino group in a simple peptide. A number of competitive inhibitors of the enzyme prevent this specific reaction. Further substitution occurs at residue 7 but prior modification of 41 appears to be mandatory. This work provides an excellent example of the delicate use of a relatively non-specific reagent under conditions where the specificity is supplied by the protein. The ability to draw firm conclusions then depends entirely on careful characterization of the reaction products. In the present instance it is clear that lysyl residue 41 is at, or close to, the active site of the enzyme.

The interaction of the enzyme with haloacetates is another example of the same approach. Barnard and Stein (1959) have shown that a major product of the reaction involving bromoacetate is an enzymically inactive derivative

5

containing a carboxymethyl group on the histidyl residue in position 119. In an extensive series of experiments using iodoacetic acid, Gundlach, Stein and Moore (1959) and Crestfield, Stein and Moore (1963) have shown that alkylation of histidine 119 occurs on nitrogen-1 of the imidazole ring. A minor component of the reaction mixture contains a nitrogen-3 substituted histidyl residue at position 12. This derivative shows only a trace of residual activity. Surprisingly, the substitutions at these two positions are mutually exclusive, and the whole effect is seen only with iodoacetate ion and not with iodoacetamide. The peculiar reactivity of these two residues is related to the conformation of the catalytically active protein and is destroyed by denaturation (Stark et al., 1961). The reactions are also slowed down or stopped in the presence of divalent anions such as sulphate or phosphate. However, the enzyme is catalytically active even in very high concentrations of sulphate ion (Doscher and Richards, 1963). The relation of iodoacetate reaction to enzymic activity is considered below in the discussion by Mathias. A more detailed description of Crestfield's experiments will be given by Moore (1964) at the anniversary meeting of the Société de Chimie Biologique.

Denatured ribonuclease reacts readily with iodoacetate (or iodoacetamide) to form derivatives involving the methionyl residues. Alkylation takes place at the sulphur atom to yield a sulphonium salt. This reaction occurs very slowly or not at all with the native enzyme (Neumann et al., 1962; Crestfield et al., 1963). The four methionyl side chains are masked, or unavailable, in the absence of denaturing conditions. They appear to play an important role in maintaining the conformation of the protein. Sulphonium salt formation in certain of these residues causes marked structural change and loss of catalytic activity. There is no evidence that any of the methionines serve as contact residues at the active site. They are considered below in relation to RNase-S.

The tyrosines represent another class of residues that appears to have an important structural role. The peculiar ionization and spectral properties of three of the six groups were discovered by Shugar (1952). Subsequent studies (Tanford et al., 1955; Bigelow, 1961) have shown the interrelation between the native structure and the anomalous properties and how both are affected by changes in the solvent environment. From this work it is clear that three tyrosine residues are distinguishable from each other and from simple phenols in aqueous solution. These three anomalous residues are clearly not so accessible to the solvent as are the other groups of this class.

More recently, Cha and Scheraga (1963) have checked the chemical reactivity of the phenolic groups with the iodination reaction. Both mono- and di-iodotyrosines can be formed depending on the extent of the reaction. In the absence of denaturing conditions it was found that the tyrosine residues in positions 25 and 97 do not react with iodine. These are presumably two of the three residues whose spectral properties are anomalous. The third residue with an abnormal phenolic ionization is close enough to the aqueous environment to react normally with iodine. The iodination of the ring occurs ortho to the phenolic hydroxyl group. It does seem odd that a large attacking group such as I_3^- can get so close to a hydroxyl function which is having difficulty dissociating a proton. If the effect on ionization is electrostatic rather than steric, then the required local negative potential would surely repel the iodinating reagent.

MODIFICATION OF RIBONUCLEASE-S

Ribonuclease-S is itself a derivative of the native enzyme produced by limited proteolysis (Figure 1). The only known change in covalent structure is the loss of the peptide bond between residues 20 and 21. The ability to separate and recombine the two parts (designated S-protein, and S-peptide respec-

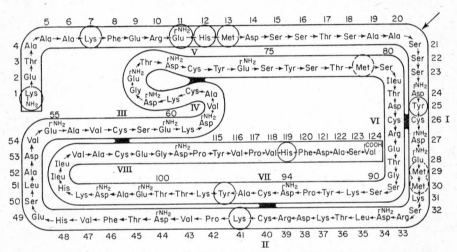

FIGURE 1. Diagram of the covalent structure of bovine pancreatic ribonuclease-A (Smyth, Stein and Moore, 1963). The heavy circles enclose some of the residues that have been specifically altered by chemical modification. The nature of the modifications and the effects produced are discussed in the text. The arrow at the upper right indicates the bond cleaved by proteolysis to yield ribonuclease-S (Richards and Vithayathil, 1959). The smaller component of the latter substance, residues 1–20, is designated S-peptide. The other component, residues 21–124, is referred to as S-protein.

tively) of this molecule has proved useful. Two factors of general interest are: (1) the very strong binding between the two parts at neutral pH and ambient temperature; and (2) the reappearance of enzymic activity which accompanies this interaction. The two effects may not be directly connected.

Richards and Vithayathil (1960) have summarized the results of a series of chemical modifications of the functional groups on the smaller component, S-peptide. Substantial changes in the net charge of the peptide, through acetylation or esterification, have little effect on either the binding or the activity of the complex. However, the methionine residue in position 13 makes an important contribution to the interaction. Conversion to a sulphonium salt by reaction with iodoacetate lowers the peptide association constant by a factor of at least a thousand. However, the catalytic activity of the complex is not markedly affected. There is tentative evidence that the amide group in position 11 is required for catalytic activity but has no influence on the binding (Vithayathil and Richards, 1961a). Crestfield *et al.* (1963) have inferred that histidine 12 is either at or very close to the active

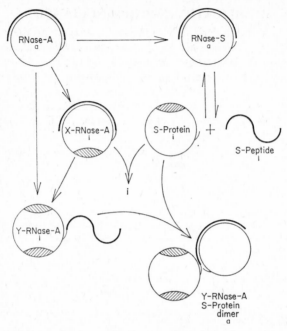

FIGURE 2. Schematic diagram of the ribonuclease system. The irreversible conversion of RNase-A to RNase-S is shown at the top, followed on the right by the reversible dissociation of RNase-S into S-peptide and S-protein. Altered forms of RNase-A are shown on the left which either do not, or do, result in a loosening of the amino-terminal portion of the molecule. In the former case no interaction occurs with added S-protein. In the latter a dimer may be formed which regenerates catalytic activity. The various species are indicated as either enzymically active or inactive with the small letters a and i. The shaded areas are the regions of presumed structural alteration.

centre. It is interesting that an adjacent residue (methionine 13) can be so drastically modified without marked influence on the enzymic activity.

A schematic diagram of the ribonuclease system is shown in Figure 2. The reaction of the protein and peptide components shown on the right has just been discussed. The protein component can also be used to investigate the state of association of the amino-terminal portion of the native enzyme (Richards and Vithayathil, 1960). For example, treatment with strong alkali rapidly causes complete loss of activity in RNase-A and considerable disruption of the native conformation. If this denatured material is mixed with S-protein, full enzymic activity is restored, the "tail" of the opened molecule complexing with the undenatured S-protein. Other drastic modifications such as complete acetylation of amino groups or esterification of carboxyl groups give similar results. More subtle inactivation, however, may produce a different effect. The fully guanidinated material described by Klee and Richards (1957), although itself inactive, will not regenerate activity in the presence of S-protein. Denaturation of the guanidinated preparation permits recovery of activity. A similar observation was made with the carboxymethyl histidine-119 derivative of Crestfield (Vithayathil and Richards, 1961b). In the latter two cases the absence of enzymic activity in the derivatives is not associated with any conformational change sufficiently drastic to free the amino-terminal portion of the molecule. This is evidence to confirm that the altered residues are a part of, or very close to, the active site of the enzyme.

In addition to chemical modification of the functional groups, attempts have been made to define, by degradation and by synthesis, that portion of S-peptide which is essential for binding and activity. Following the initial observations (Richards, 1958) on activity loss after tryptic or chymotryptic digestion, Allende and Richards (1962) made a more detailed study of the reaction with trypsin. Of the two susceptible bonds, 7–8 and 10–11, the latter is split much more rapidly and the two decapeptides can be obtained in fair yield. These peptides, either separately or combined, showed no ability to regenerate activity when mixed with S-protein. No interaction of any sort was detected at the usual assay concentration ($\sim 10^{-6}$ M). (Apparently some proteolysis of S-protein by trypsin can occur without abolishing the inter-action with the peptide; however, the picture here is complicated.) A minor component in some ribonuclease preparations lacks the amino-terminal lysine and will give a 19 residue S-peptide otherwise identical with the normal one (Gordillo et al., 1962). Two stages of the Edman degradation were applied to a diguanidinated derivative of S-peptide. The product showed substantial enzymic activity with little change in binding to S-protein (M. Doscher, un-published results). Attempts to get smaller identifiable peptides by degrada-tion from the amino terminal end with leucine amino peptidase have so far proved to be unsuccessful.

Recently Potts, Young and Anfinsen (1963) have studied the degradation of S-peptide with carboxypeptidase-A. The removal of the five carboxyl terminal amino acids yielded a fifteen residue peptide which still showed full activity when mixed with S-protein at a 1:1 molar ratio and assayed with RNA. Whether or not there is any change at all in binding constant cannot be stated with certainty since the differential binding of RNA biases the estimate of the protein–peptide equilibrium constant.

Figure 3 summarizes these degradative studies. The maximum number of required residues cannot be greater than those in positions 3 through 15.

Work on the synthesis of S-peptide has been reported recently by Hof-mann et al. (1963), and by Rocchi, Marchiori and Scoffone (1963) and Marchiori, Rocchi and Scoffone (1963). The complete 20 residue unit has not yet been assembled but interaction has been observed between S-protein and some of the smaller pieces of S-peptide. Some of this work is summarized in Figure 3. It is seen that a peptide containing residues 1 through 13 is capable of regenerating activity with the protein component although the binding constant is considerably reduced. Comparing this result with that of Potts *et al.* (1963), it appears that residues 14 and 15 play an important role in the binding but are not directly connected with the activity of the complex.

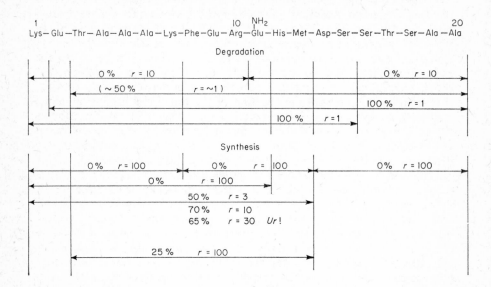

FIGURE 3. Summary of data on the fragments of S-peptide obtained either by degradation or synthesis. The individual peptides were assayed with a fixed quantity of S-protein. The numbers indicate activity observed as a percent of that shown by an equivalent quantity of RNase-S. The symbol r gives the molar ratio of peptide fragment to S-protein used in the assay mixture. The substrate was ribonucleic acid unless otherwise indicated. (Ur! = cyclic uridylic acid.) Estimates of the peptide–protein binding constants can be obtained from data on activity as a function of r. In general, structural changes in the peptide may be expected to alter the binding constant or the catalytic activity of the complex or both. Literature references to the various studies are given in the text.

A 13 residue peptide has also been produced in another degradative study employing cyanogen bromide cleavage of the native enzyme (Parks, Baranick and Wold, 1963). The carboxyl-terminal residue in this case is homoserine lactone rather than methionine. High activities are obtained for the complex with S-protein but the binding constant appears to be lower than with the methionine-containing tridecapeptide. This observation is further evidence of the importance of methionine 13 in providing an important part of the binding energy for the peptide–protein interaction.

REACTION IN MICELLES

The low reactivities of methionyl and certain tyrosyl residues in ribonuclease are examples of the masking of functional groups, a phenomenon found in many proteins. A commonly offered explanation is that such groups are buried in "hydrophobic regions in the interior of the macromolecule." The implication of the statement appears to be that the kinetic parameters are altered by the hydrocarbon environment, by steric effects or by both. Micelles provide small hydrocarbon volumes which have dimensions comparable to those of macromolecules and are dispersed in aqueous solution. In principle, one could alter the kinetics of a bimolecular reaction simply by separation of the reactants, one being excluded from the micelle and the other strongly absorbed. The most clear-cut examples of this effect come from systems where one of the reactants has a formal charge of the same sign as that of the micelle. Thus, complex formation between divalent copper ions and a neutral porphyrin is strongly inhibited in the presence of a cationic detergent (Lowe and Phillips, 1961); the reaction of 1-fluorodinitrobenzene (FDNB) and glycylglycine is restricted to the aqueous phase in the presence of sodium dodecyl sulphate since the amine anion is excluded from the micelle (Herries et al., 1964). For these two examples, the converse effect, rate enhancement, is observed if micelles of opposite charge are used. Less easily explained is the lack of kinetic change for systems where the two reactants are uncharged even though the partition coefficients are very different. The free base form of glycineamide is polar enough to be excluded from the micelle interior while FDNB partitions strongly in favour of the micelle. From a reaction in pure aqueous solution to one in a detergent concentration such that 75% of the total FDNB is absorbed to the micelles, there is a change in reaction rate of less than 5% (Herries et al., 1964). If one assumes that the reaction occurs on the surface of the micelle, then some fortuitous cancellation of effects must be invoked to explain the lack of detectable effect on the reaction kinetics. Since charge separation is involved, the rate in the non-polar interior region would almost certainly be much lower. The available evidence on this subject is insufficient to provide a clear picture of all the factors involved.

So far these studies have reinforced the general observations made on the modification of proteins. A particular amino acid residue may exhibit strong interaction with other parts of the protein and contribute to the stability of the native structure; a functional group located on this residue may or may not have altered chemical reactivity depending entirely on the nature of the local environment and of the reagent used.

REFERENCES

Allende, J. E. and Richards, F. M. (1962). *Biochemistry* **1**, 295.

Barnard, E. A. and Stein, W. D. (1959). *J. mol. Biol.* **1**, 339, 350.

Bigelow, C. C. (1961). *J. biol. Chem.* **236**, 1706.

Cha, C. Y. and Scheraga, H. A. (1963). *J. biol. Chem.* **238**, 2958, 2965.

Crestfield, A. M., Stein, W. H. and Moore, S. (1963). *J. biol. Chem.* **238**, 2413, 2421.

Doscher, M. S. and Richards, F. M. (1963). *J. biol. Chem.* **238**, 2399.

Gordillo, G., Vithayathil, P. J. and Richards, F. M. (1962). *Yale J. Biol. Med.* **34**, 582.

Gundlach, H. G., Stein, W. H. and Moore, S. (1959). *J. biol. Chem.* **234**, 1754.

Herries, D. G., Bishop, W. and Richards, F. M. (1964). *J. phys. Chem.* **68**, 1842.

Hirs, C. H. W. (1962). Brookhaven Symposia in Biology, No. 15, p. 154.

Hofmann, K., Finn, F., Haas, W., Smithers, M. J., Wolman, Y. and Yanaihara, N. (1963). *J. Amer. chem. Soc.* **85**, 833.

Klee, W, A. and Richards, F. M. (1957). *J. biol. Chem.* **229**, 489.

Kunitz, M. (1940). *J. gen. Physiol.* **24**, 15.

Lowe, M. B. and Phillips, J. N. (1961). *Nature, Lond.* **190**, 262.

Marchiori, F., Rocchi, R. and Scoffone, E. (1963). *Gazz. chim. Ital.* **93**, 834.

Moore, S. (1964). Cinquantenaire de la Société de Chimie Biologique, April 6, 1964.

Neumann, N. P., Moore, S. and Stein, W. H. (1962). *Biochemistry* **1**, 68.

Parks, J. M., Baranick, M. B. and Wold, F. (1963). *J. Amer. chem. Soc.* **85**, 3519.

Potts, J. T., Young, D. M. and Anfinsen, C. B. (1963). *J. biol. Chem.* **238**, 2593.

Richards, F. M. (1958). *Proc. nat. Acad. Sci., Wash.* **44**, 162.

Richards, F. M. and Vithayathil, P. J. (1959). *J. biol. Chem.* **234**, 1459.

Richards, F. M. and Vithayathil, P. J. (1960). *Brookhaven Symposia in Biology*, No. 13, p. 115.

Rocchi, R., Marchiori, F. and Scoffone, E. (1963). *Gazz. chim. Ital.* **93**, 823.

Shugar, D. (1952). *Biochem. J.* **52**, 141.

Smyth, D. G., Stein, W. H. and Moore, S. (1963). *J. biol. Chem.* **238**, 227.

Stark, G. R., Stein, W. H. and Moore, S. (1961). *J. biol. Chem.* **236**, 436.

Tanford, C., Hauenstein, J. D. and Rands, D. G. (1955). *J. Amer. chem. Soc.* **77**, 6409.

Vithayathil, P. J. and Richards, F. M. (1961a). *J. biol. Chem.* **236**, 1380.

Vithayathil, P. J. and Richards, F. M. (1961b). *J. biol. Chem.* **236**, 1386.

DISCUSSION

A. P. MATHIAS: Dr. Richards has found that ribonuclease is active in the crystalline state. Has it been possible to observe any conformational change when the substrate diffuses into the crystal?

F. M. RICHARDS: Yes, we have studied the activity of ribonuclease-S in the crystalline state. The major part of the work by M. Doscher on this problem has appeared in the *Journal of Biological Chemistry* in July 1963. The general qualitative conclusion is that the molecules in the crystal lattice interior to the surface are, in fact, catalytically active. One can arrange a crystal on the X-ray camera in such a position that it is completely immersed in a liquid which can be flowed over the crystal while the diffraction pattern is being observed. When substrate (cytidine 2′,3′-phosphate) is added to the liquid, the intensities of some of the X-ray reflections are changed with little or no changes in unit cell dimensions. The intensity changes were reversed when the substrate was washed out of the crystal. The significance of these intensity changes will probably remain unclear until the complete three dimensional structure of the enzyme is known. Speculation on the conformation changes during catalytic activity is unwarranted on the basis of these observations alone.

In addition to RNase-S we have looked at crystalline carboxypeptidase-A and rabbit muscle aldolase. The first appears to be catalytically active and the second not in the crystals with which we are working. The lack of activity in the aldolase crystals is attributed to the great sensitivity of the reaction to ionic strength rather than to any effect of the crystal lattice. Mr. Florante Quiocho is attempting to work out the kinetic parameters of crystalline carboxypeptidase-A for comparison with the values in solution. Water or dilute salt solutions which can be used with carboxypeptidase are much more convenient solvents than the very concentrated ammonium sulphate solution required to keep the ribonuclease crystals from dissolving.

Alkylation of the Dimer of Ribonuclease

S. Moore

Rockefeller Institute, New York, New York, U.S.A.

The experiments of Richards on ribonuclease-S and the S-peptide have been of great value in the interpretation of a number of results obtained with the intact enzyme. The formulation of the dimer of ribonuclease is a case in point. The most recent observations along this line are those of Crestfield and Fruchter (1964). They have obtained evidence on the nature of the dimer by studying the products of its alkylation by iodoacetate.

If the dimer is considered as a combination of two molecules of ribonuclease in which the amino-terminal segment of one molecule is adsorbed on the main portion of the other, and vice versa, the combination may be represented as in Figure 1.

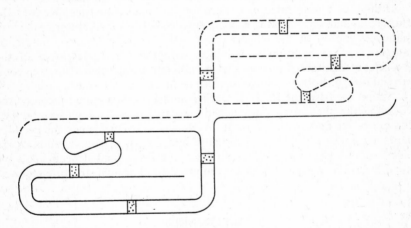

FIGURE 1. Hypothetical formulation of the dimer of ribonuclease (from Crestfield, Stein and Moore, 1962).

Considered in conjunction with the knowledge that two histidine residues are involved in each active site, the above hypothesis assumes that the active site in each half of the dimer includes histidine-12 and histidine-119 residues from two different monomer molecules. The alternative assumption would be that two monomers adsorb to one another without the unfolding of the active site in each.

13

Experimental evidence in favour of the first hypothesis has been obtained by examining the products of the alkylation reaction. In ribonuclease, iodo-acetate reacts at pH 5·5 with one *or* the other of the two histidine residues at an active site (Crestfield, Stein and Moore, 1963); no *di*-substituted derivative (carboxymethylated at both histidine-12 and histidine-119) is formed by alkylation of the monomer. But if each active site in the dimer is constructed from parts of two molecules, as formulated in Figure 1, the either-or reaction with each pair of histidine residues would, on a probability basis, lead to the formation of an appreciable amount of a molecule of ribonuclease in which the histidine residues at both positions 12 and 119 were alkylated. Crestfield and Fruchter have obtained a disubstituted product, in confirmation of this formulation.

Your Chairman has also asked me whether there are any developments in our analytical procedures which would be of practical concern to users of amino acid analysers. We share the common wish to analyse smaller samples without loss of precision. Dr. Crestfield now has on test a photometer utilizing a flow cell of the type which he has described (Crestfield, 1963) and with a 2-cm light path. The modification increases the sensitivity of the analyser tenfold; analyses of peptides are now being run with 10^{-8} moles per sample. This scale of operation meets most of our current needs.

As the use of accelerated procedure for amino acid analysis increases the output per analyser, attention is being devoted in several laboratories to auto-matic integration of the effluent curves. We have on test two automatic integrators; one built in co-operation with the Electronics Shop of the Rockefeller Institute, and the other a completely independent unit of com-mercial design. Both provide direct print-out of the area of each peak, with correction for base-line level. An earlier model which we used recorded the output of the photometer on punched tape for use with a high-speed digital computer. We find direct print-out much more convenient than the need for computer time, albeit brief. Automatic integration, of course, adds to the investment in equipment; the returns on the investment depend upon the number of such analyses which a given problem in protein structure requires.

REFERENCES

Crestfield, A. M. (1963). *Analyt. Chem.* **35**, 1762.
Crestfield, A. M. and Fruchter, R. (1964). *Fed. Proc.* (in press)
Crestfield, A. M., Stein, W. H. and Moore, S. (1962). *Arch. Biochem. Biophys.* **217**, Suppl. 1, 217.
Crestfield, A. M., Stein, W. H. and Moore, S. (1963). *J. biol. Chem.* **238**, 2421.

A Three-dimensional Electron Density Map of Ribonuclease at a Resolution of 4Å

D. Harker, J. Bello, D. R. Harris, H. H. Mills,
R. Parthasarathy, and F. E. DeJarnette

Roswell Park Memorial Institute, Buffalo, New York, U.S.A.

Modification II of crystalline bovine pancreatic ribonuclease (monoclinic, space group $P2_1$, 2 molecules per cell, $a = 30 \cdot 13$ Å, $b = 38 \cdot 24$ Å, $c = 53 \cdot 06$ Å, $\beta = 105 \cdot 77°$) was the experimental material. Specimens were prepared by soaking in 75% 2-methyl-2,4-pentanediol (MPD), with or without "heavy-atom dyes". We succeeded in preparing the following heavy-atom derivatives.

(1) Platinum *cis* Diglycine, approximately 8:1†.
(2) Platinum *cis* Diglycine, approximately 6:1.
(3) Platinum *cis* Diglycine, approximately 4:1.
(4) Platinum trisethylenediamine tetrachloride.
(5) Uranyl sulphosalicylate together with platinum trisethylenediamine tetrachloride.

The intensities of the X-ray diffraction maxima were measured for the five dyed and the undyed crystals, using the original goniostat (Furnas and Harker, 1955) mounted on a General Electric XRD-3 Spectrogoniometer and Cu$K\alpha$ radiation monochromatized by a balanced pair of nickel and cobalt filters. All reflections corresponding to interplanar spacings greater than 4 Å were measured.

From each intensity the magnitude of a coefficient in the Fourier series for the electron density of the corresponding crystal can be calculated, but not its phase. However, by combining the data obtained from the undyed crystal and the various dyed crystals it is possible to find the positions of the heavy atoms in the latter (Kartha *et al.*, 1963) and, using this information, to estimate the phases of the Fourier coefficients for the former (Harker, 1956; Dickerson, Kendrew and Strandberg, 1961). Special programmes were written to carry out the required computations‡ on the IBM 7090, and phases were thus assigned to the Fourier coefficients of the undyed crystal. The electron density function was then calculated.

† 8:1, 6:1, and 4:1 refer to the ratios of dye molecules to protein molecules.
‡ In the course of these computations, the heavy atom positions and "occupancies" were refined.

A representation of this electron density function appears in Figure 1. The function was calculated on thirty parallel sections normal to the *b*-axis at intervals of *b*/30. Each section covers a parallelogram with sides of length *a* and *c*/2. (In the figure the *a*-axis is pointed toward the viewer and the *c*-axis runs from left to right.) The model thus exhibits only half of a unit cell; the other half of the cell is related to this half by the operation of a twofold

FIGURE 1.

screw axis set half way along the *a*-axis parallel to *b*. On each section contours of equal electron density were drawn on glass plates: one at a very high level and two lower ones. Using the contours on each section as a guide, coloured disks were placed on the glass sheets so as to indicate possibly continuous three-dimensional regions of high density. The distance between sections is about 1·3 Å and the other dimensions of the model, while not to correct scale, are such as to provide a not too badly distorted image.

The following features can be found in the model, and appear fairly well in the figure.

(a) There are *no* continuous regions of high density with the correct dimensions to correspond to lengths of α helix; this is to be expected from a correct model, in view of the physicochemical studies on ribonuclease.

(b) The continuous three-dimensional regions that do appear are about the correct dimensions to represent extended polypeptide chains.

(c) It is *not* possible to correlate the length of the continuous high-density regions with the known length of the polypeptide chain in ribonuclease which consists of 124 amino acid residues.

(d) There appear to be more "cross-points" in the continuous regions than can be put into correspondence with the four disulphide cross-links in the ribonuclease molecule.

It is obvious that more data and computation are required before an electron density function can be constructed which will be directly interpretable in terms of the structure of the ribonuclease molecule. Work along these lines is going forward, and we hope soon to have an image of the electron density in crystals of ribonuclease II at a resolution of 3 Å.

REFERENCES

Dickerson, R. E., Kendrew, J. C. and Strandberg, B. E. (1961). *Acta cryst.* **14**, 1188.

Furnas, T. C., Jr. and Harker, D. (1955). *Rev. sci. Instrum.* **26**, 449.

Harker, D. (1956). *Acta cryst.* **9**, 1.

Kartha, G., Bello, J., Harker, D. and DeJarnette, F. E. (1963). *In* "Aspects of Protein Structure", ed. by G. N. Ramachandran, p. 13. Academic Press, London.

Studies on the Active Site and Mechanism of Action of Bovine Pancreatic Ribonuclease

A. P. MATHIAS, A. DEAVIN and B. R. RABIN

Department of Biochemistry, University College London, England

The determination in detail of the mechanism of a reaction catalysed by an enzyme, and the identification of the numerous groups in the protein which are involved in its interaction with the substrate, present formidable problems that can be solved only by pursuing several different lines of investigation. Confidence in a postulated mechanism is strengthened by the extent to which the conclusions, reached independently by different approaches, support one another. The work of Moore and Stein and their collaborators, of Richards, and many other workers, coupled with experiments carried out at University College by Deavin, Findlay, Herries, Mathias, Rabin and Ross, have led us to propose a mechanism for the mode of action of bovine pancreatic ribonuclease which involves two histidine residues in the enzyme.

The first indication of the importance of the histidines of ribonuclease came from experiments on the inactivation of the enzyme by photo-oxidation (Weil and Seibles, 1955). The inactivation of ribonuclease by reaction with haloacetic acids at pH values near neutrality was attributed to alkylation of an imidazole group (Barnard and Stein, 1959). Crestfield, Stein and Moore (1963) showed that, at pH 5·5, ribonuclease reacts with iodoacetate ions to give a product of which about 85% is an inactive mono-carboxymethylated derivative in which histidine-119 is substituted on the 1 position. The remaining 15% is carboxymethylated on the 3 position of histidine-12 and is also virtually inactive.

We have investigated the alkylation reaction in some detail, using the loss of enzyme activity with cytidine 2′,3′-phosphate as substrate, as a method for following the reaction. First it was established that, at constant pH, temperature, ionic strength and iodoacetate concentration, the reaction is first order with respect to the concentration of enzyme. This may be seen from the log plots shown in Figure 1. It is also first order in iodoacetate concentration and Figure 2 shows the variation of the apparent first order rate constant for enzyme inactivation with iodoacetate concentration. By using a Ag/AgI electrode to follow the rate of liberation of iodide ions, it was shown that, for each mole of enzyme inactivated, one mole of iodide ions appears, thus confirming that 1:1 reaction occurs.

Normally the inactivation of ribonuclease by iodoacetate is carried out with a large excess of the latter, and the apparent first order rate constant for the loss of enzyme activity can be used as a convenient measure of the velocity of the reaction. The variation of the rate of inactivation with pH is shown in Figure 3.

19

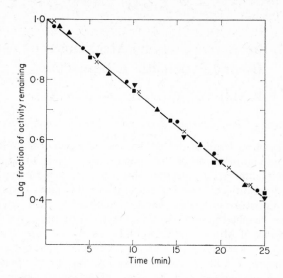

FIGURE 1. Inhibition of ribonuclease by iodoacetate, at 40°C. $I = 0.02$, pH 5·25, iodo-acetate concentration 0·02 M. Ribonuclease concentrations (mg/ml): ●, 0·965; ■, 0·772; ▲, 0·579; ▼, 0·386; ×, 0·193.

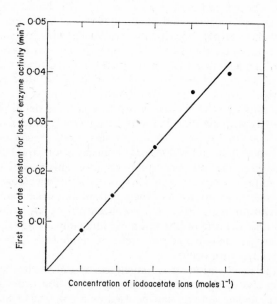

FIGURE 2. Variation of the rate of alkylation of ribonuclease with iodoacetate concentration at 40°C. $I = 0.05$, pH 6·00, ribonuclease 73 μM.

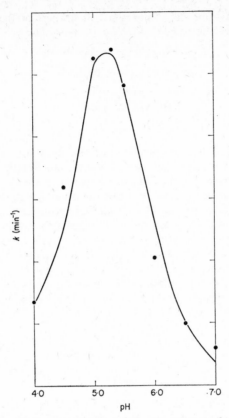

FIGURE 3. Variation of the apparent first order rate constant for the inactivation of ribonuclease by iodoacetate with pH. 40°C, $I = 0.02$, iodoacetate 0.02 M. The points are experimental, and the line calculated using values shown in Table I.

The data can be interpreted satisfactorily in terms of the reaction scheme

$$\overset{K_b}{EH_2 \rightleftharpoons} \overset{K_a}{EH \rightleftharpoons} E$$

$$\bar{k} \downarrow \quad + \text{ Iodoacetate}$$
$$\text{Inactive enzyme}$$

where K_b and K_a are dissociation constants of two groups on the enzyme and $\bar{k}$ is the pH-independent apparent first order rate constant for the reaction of the species EH with iodoacetate.

The measured rate constant, k, is related to $\bar{k}$ by the equation

$$k = \frac{\bar{k}}{1 + \dfrac{[H^+]}{K_b} + \dfrac{K_a}{[H^+]}}$$

The values for the constants have been calculated and are shown in Table I.

TABLE I. Experimentally Determined Parameters of the Alkylation
Reaction at 40°C. I, 0·02 and Iodoacetate 0·02 M

$$\bar{k} = 0·10 \pm 0·04 \, \text{min}^{-1}$$
$$pK_b = 4·85 \pm 0·13$$
$$pK_a = 5·55 \pm 0·13$$

The curve in Figure 3 was calculated on the basis of these values and is in good agreement with the experimental points. The kinetic data suggest that reaction of the enzyme with iodoacetate ions requires one of a pair of groups in the enzyme to be in the acid form and the other one in the base form. The nature of the products indicates that both these groups are imidazole residues and the measured values of the pKs, although at the lower end of the range expected for imidazoles in the side chain of histidine residues at this temperature and ionic strength, confirm this identification. Presumably the positively charged imidazolium group binds the iodoacetate by electrostatic attraction, holding it in a suitable position for attack by the imidazole group acting as a nucleophile (Figure 4). This would explain the lack of reaction

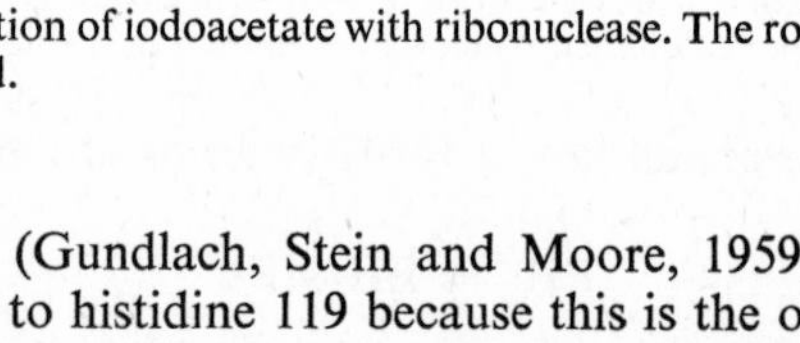

FIGURE 4. The interaction of iodoacetate with ribonuclease. The roles of the two imidazole residues can be reversed.

with iodoacetamide (Gundlach, Stein and Moore, 1959). It is tempting to assign the lower pK to histidine 119 because this is the one that is alkylated predominantly. This cannot be done with any confidence because of the probable differences in the intrinsic reactivities of the two residues and the fact that the calculated pK's are macroscopic and not microscopic constants.

The assumption that histidines 12 and 119 form part of the active site is supported by the observation that the enzyme is protected against alkylation by competitive inhibitors. A range of substances has been investigated as inhibitors of the hydrolysis of cytidine 2′,3′-phosphate catalysed by ribonuclease, and of the alkylation of the enzyme. Both reactions have been studied at pH 5·2 with $I = 0·02$ and at 25°C. There is good agreement between the K_i values found for each inhibitor in both reactions, and some of the results are listed in Table II.

TABLE II. K_i Value for Inhibition of the Alkylation of Ribonuclease by Iodoacetate and Hydrolysis of the Cytidine 2′,3′-phosphate at 25°C, $I = 0.02$, pH 5.2

Inhibitor	$K_i \times 10^6$ (M)	
	Alkylation reaction	Hydrolysis of cyclic phosphate
Cytidine 2′-phosphate	0.65 ± 0.31	1.87 ± 0.6
Cytidine 3′-phosphate	7.3 ± 4.1	15.9 ± 2.4
Pyrophosphate	4.91 ± 2.5	7.6 ± 3.6
Deoxythymidine 3′-phosphate benzyl ester	3.83 ± 0.7	1.03 ± 0.82

These compounds are competitive inhibitors of the catalysis and the marked similarity of their K_i values in the alkylation reaction and in the enzymic activity of ribonuclease is a strong argument in support of the idea that histidines 12 and 119 form part of the active site.

The existence of a pH optimum in an enzyme reaction is usually explained by supposing a requirement for at least two ionizing groups for activity, with the active enzyme containing one group in the acid form and one in the base form. The identification of these groups is made easier if it is known to which charge type they belong. That is, whether they are neutral acids whose dissociations involve charge separation

$$AH \rightleftharpoons A^- + H^+$$

or cationic acids

$$BH^+ \rightleftharpoons B + H^+$$

A striking difference between these two types of acid is found in the changes of their pKs which occur when water is replaced by an organic solvent. If an organic solvent is added to an aqueous solution, the pK values of neutral acids are increased while those of cationic acids are unchanged or slightly decreased. The extent of the change is dictated by the nature and concentration of the organic solvent and the charge type, and not by the actual structure of the acid. The finding that ribonuclease is active in high concentrations of organic solvents (Findlay, Mathias and Rabin, 1962a) has enabled the development of a method of general use for determining the charge type of groups at the active site of an enzyme. This involves the measurement of the pH activity curves in the presence and absence of organic solvents in a series of cationic buffers and a series of neutral acid buffers. The method is valid only if the main effect of the presence of the organic solvent is to cause shifts in pKs determined by the charge types of the acid. Hence acids of a given charge type will show the same shift whether they are buffers or groups on a protein. The experimental conditions must be so arranged that the effect of the presence of an organic solvent on the enzyme activity is confined mainly to shifts in the pKs of groups in the "active centre", and in the buffers employed. Alteration of activity due to changes in protein conformation, the binding of substrate to the enzyme, and solvation effects in the transition state, can be largely eliminated in the case of ribonuclease. On the basis of these assumptions it is possible to predict the differences between the pH

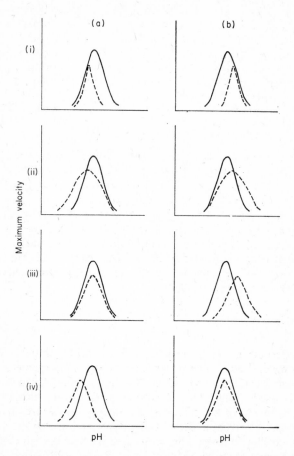

FIGURE 5. Theoretical pH (water)–activity curves in water (full lines) and in a water–solvent mixture (broken lines) for the four possible ionizing pairs at the active centre of an enzyme: (i) neutral–cation, (ii) cation–neutral, (iii) neutral–neutral, (iv) cation–cation in two series of buffers, (a) neutral acid buffers and (b) cationic acid buffers. The ordinate is a measure of maximum velocity. The abscissa is the pH measured in water.

activity curves in aqueous organic solvents and in water for the four possible combinations of ionizing pairs at the active centre of an enzyme. This is shown in Figure 5. There are distinct differences between each of the four possible combinations. The pH–activity curves of ribonuclease with cytidine 2′,3′-phosphate as substrate have been determined in water, 50% (v/v)

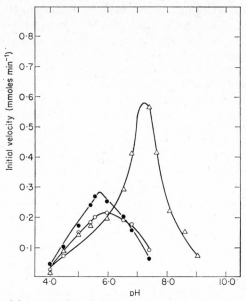

FIGURE 6. pH–activity curves for ribonuclease in a series of neutral-acid buffers in water (△); in 50% (v/v) dioxan (●) and 50% (v/v) formamide (○). Substrate concentration 0·05 M, ribonuclease 0·0125 mg/ml.

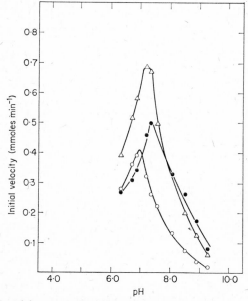

FIGURE 7. pH–activity curves for ribonuclease in a series of cationic-acid buffers in water (△); in 50% (v/v) dioxan (●), and 50% (v/v) formamide (○). Substrate and ribonuclease concentration as in Figure 6.

dioxan, and 50% (v/v) formamide in a series of cationic acid and neutral acid buffers. Both formamide and dioxan shift the curve to lower values in neutral acid buffers, but have little effect in cationic buffers (Figures 6 and 7). The resemblance between the behaviour of ribonuclease and case (iv) in Figure 5 is striking, and provides convincing evidence that the catalytic site of ribonuclease contains two cationic acids.

The kinetic parameters for the hydrolysis of cytidine 2′,3′-phosphate vary with pH in a manner compatible with the assumption that the variation of activity with pH curves is controlled by two ionizing groups at the active site, one required in the acid form, the other in the base form (Herries, Mathias and Rabin, 1962). There is good reason to believe that in this system K_m represents a true dissociation constant for the enzyme–substrate complex, and this simplifies the calculation of the pK values of the groups at the active site—both in the free enzyme and in the enzyme–substrate complex (Table III).

TABLE III. Dissociation Constants of Groups at the Active Site of Ribonuclease; 25°C, $I = 0.20$

	Free enzyme		Enzyme–substrate complex	
pK_b	5.22 ± 0.20		pK_b'	6.30 ± 0.09
pK_a	6.78 ± 0.20		pK_a'	8.10 ± 0.09

It has been demonstrated that the two groups at the active site are cationic acids, and their pK values, summarized in Table III, suggest that these groups are imidazole residues. If one may assume that the pK values for the enzyme–substrate complex are as shown in Table III, and not reversed, the binding of the substrate to the enzyme causes both pKs to increase. This indicates that neither group in the base form can bind directly to the substrate. Yet it is probable that one of the groups at the active site is in the base form.

Ribonuclease catalyses the attack of a wide variety of hydroxylic compounds, as well as water, on cytidine 2′,3′-phosphate. The relative effectiveness of a series of alcohols as attacking agents cannot be explained if the alcohol reacting with the cyclic phosphate is a free solvent molecule. It must be bound to the active site by complex interactions, one of which involves the hydroxyl group. Water molecules would also bind at this site. Of the two imidazoles at the active site, one in the base form appears not to be bound directly to the cyclic phosphate substrate. However, it would be available to bind to the attacking water or alcohol. Hydrogen-bonding of the hydroxylic compound to the imidazole residue would enhance its nucleophilic reactivity and serve to orient it in its approach to the phosphorous atom.

It will be seen from Table II that cytidine 2′-phosphate binds to ribonuclease more strongly than cytidine 3′-phosphate. The 2′-oxygen will have a greater density of electrons in the 2'-phosphate than in the 3'-phosphate. This suggests that a positively charged group in the enzyme interacts with the 2'-oxygen.

With these facts as a basis, it is possible to formulate a mechanism for the hydrolysis of the cytidine 2',3'-phosphate (Findlay *et al.*, 1962b). The enzyme substrate complex is shown in Figure 8. I is the imidazole which, in the base form, binds the attacking hydroxylic compound. With complex alcohols

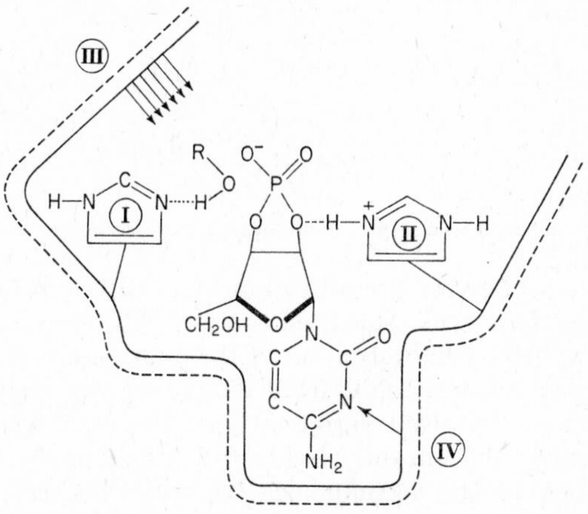

FIGURE 8. The enzyme substrate complex of ribonuclease and cytidine 2',3'-phosphate.

additional interactions occur as indicated at III. The hydrogen bond between the imidazolum residue, II, and the 2'-oxygen, weakens the P–O(2') bond and favours heterolytic fission, the bond electrons moving to the oxygen. As this happens, the proton from II adds to the 2'-oxygen making it a better leaving group. IV indicates the binding site for the pyrimidine ring which probably involves several groups on the protein, and largely determines the specificity. The transition state is depicted in Figure 9 in which the curved arrows represent the direction of the electron shifts. The catalysis arises from the synchronized shifts of the protons from one position of minimum energy to the other, thus lowering the energy barrier for the phosphoryl shift.

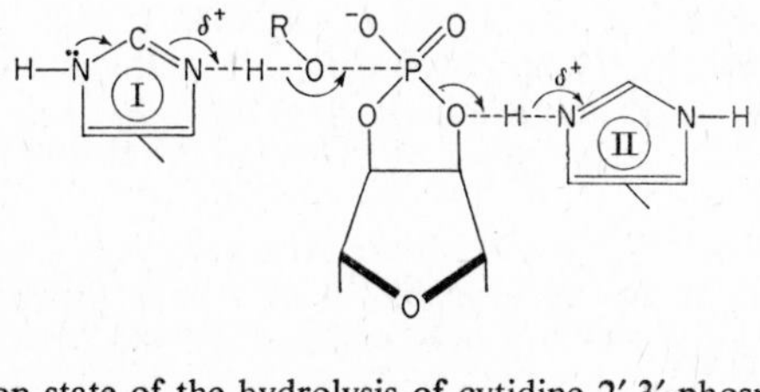

FIGURE 9. Transition state of the hydrolysis of cytidine 2',3'-phosphate in the presence of ribonuclease. The arrows show the direction of the electron shifts.

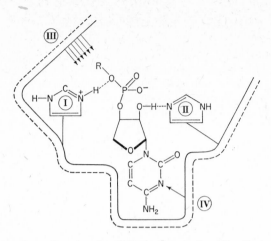

FIGURE 10. Enzyme–product complex of ribonuclease and cytidine 3'-phosphate (R = H).

The enzyme–product complex is shown in Figure 10. If R is an alkyl group, Figure 10 is also the enzyme–substrate complex of ribonuclease and esters of cytidine 3'-phosphate. The cyclization of the esters is a reversal of the pathway for the hydrolysis or alcoholysis of the cyclic phosphate.

One of the major unsolved problems is an understanding of the binding of the substrate to the enzyme. Evidently this involves a multiplicity of interactions, and may be accompanied by conformational changes in the protein. Some interactions may contribute little to the free energy of binding, but have a dominant effect on catalysis because they are required for the proper positioning of the substrate relative to catalytic centres. We are at present using spectropolarimetry to investigate this problem. Kinetic studies indicate that binding of the substrate can occur when both imidazoles of the catalytic site are in the base form. The state of ionization of at least one of the groups binding to the substrate must remain unchanged over the pH range 4–8·5.

ACKNOWLEDGMENTS

We are grateful to the Wellcome Trust, the Department of Scientific and Industrial Research, and the Medical Research Council, for grants to purchase equipment and for personal support. We thank the editors of the *Biochemical Journal* for permission to publish Figures 5–10.

REFERENCES

Barnard, E. A. and Stein, W. D. (1959). *J. mol. Biol.* **1**, 339.
Crestfield, A. M., Stein, W. H. and Moore, S. (1963). *J. biol. Chem.* **238**, 2413.
Findlay, D., Mathias, A. P. and Rabin, B. R. (1962a). *Biochem. J.* **85**, 139.
Findlay, D., Herries, D. G., Mathias, A. P., Rabin, B. R. and Ross, C. A. (1962b). *Biochem. J.* **85**, 152.
Gundlach, H. G., Stein, W. H. and Moore, S. (1959). *J. biol. Chem.* **234**, 1754.
Herries, D. G., Mathias, A. P. and Rabin, B. R. (1962). *Biochem. J.* **85**, 127.
Weil, L. and Seibles, T. S. (1955). *Arch. Biochem.* **54**, 386.

DISCUSSION

H. Witzel: We recently published a summary (for references see Witzel, 1964) of our experiments and their interpretations concerning the mechanism of the ribonuclease reaction which, we believe, follows the scheme I–VI. In this mechanism the pyrimidine base is only involved in a specific kind of catalysis, and binding of the substrates to the enzyme occurs only by a dianionic phosphate group. This requirement causes the inhibition by all dianionic monoesters and selects only those monoanionic diesters as substrates, which are able with assistance of the pyrimidine base to form an intermediate state with a dianionic pentacovalent phosphate group.

Our experiments concerning the possibility of an additional binding by the pyrimidine base did not give us any evidence for this. (a) Blocking of the potential interacting sites (e.g. 4-dimethylcytidine, N_1- and N_3-methylpseudouridine, 5,6-dihydrouridine) affects only k_2, but not K_m. (b) While the dianions of 2′- and 3′α-cytidylic acid and β-lyxouridylic acid are strong inhibitors, the monoanionic 2′,3′-cyclic phosphates which cannot form the required dianionic intermediate state for steric reasons are not substrates nor do they inhibit. The same holds for N_3-methyluridylic acid, where the intermediate state cannot be formed for electronic reasons. (c) After the relatively fast transesterification step, with CpA as substrate, cyclic Cp is formed as the product. If assumed to be still bound, it should be expected that the following hydrolysis step would be faster than the reaction started with cyclic Cp itself. But the rates are the same in both experiments, indicating that the second step is independent of the first. (d) We could show that the spectral decrease seen after mixing the dianionic mononucleotides with the enzyme, resembles the difference between the spectra of the monoester and the uncharged triester of cytidylic acid, thus indicating that the two negative charges of the phosphate group might be blocked by the enzyme—as required in our mechanism. This means that no definite evidence for base-binding can be derived from this spectral effect.

My question is whether we have any other experimental evidence for binding by the pyrimidine base, disregarding the stronger inhibition of the 2′-mononucleotides compared with the 3′-mononucleotides since this difference exists between the purine nucleotides also and might perhaps be a base induced property of the phosphate group only.

A. P. MATHIAS: The mechanism that we have proposed for the hydrolysis of cytidine 2′,3′-phosphate does not depend on the bonding of the pyrimidine ring to the enzyme. Direct experimental evidence that interaction occurs between the protein and the pyrimidine is obviously difficult to obtain. The spectral shifts that have been observed when the product, cytidine 3′-phosphate, or the inhibitor cytidine 2′-phosphate, bind to ribonuclease although not conclusive, may be an indication of binding at the pyrimidine.

On the basis of the mechanism suggested by Dr. Witzel, many compounds that should be substrates are not hydrolysed. Studies of models show that it may be possible to force the 2′-hydroxyl to form a hydrogen bond with the 2-oxygen of the pyrimidine. This involves a seven-membered ring and is under considerable strain. However, this bonding can also occur in the α-cytidine series and in lyxouridine. Esters of the 3′-phosphates of these compounds are not substrates. The marked similarity of the spectra of cytidine + deoxycytidine at pH values below 12, shows that the hydrogen bonding of 2′-OH and 2-O probably does not occur.

Dr. Witzel has postulated that in the hydrolysis of the cyclic phosphate, the attacking water molecule is hydrogen-bonded to pyrimidine oxygen. In this position access to the phosphorus is very difficult because the phosphorus is too far away and the oxygens attached to phosphorus get in the way. It is the P—(2′)-O bond which is split and the water molecule is much more likely to approach above the 3′-oxygen.

Comparisons of K_m values with these for k_2 are not readily interpreted. If multiple interactions between substrate and enzyme are necessary to bring the catalytic groups opposite to the susceptible bonds in the substrate, one would expect small changes in K_m with much larger changes in k_2. The groups in the substrate responsible for the major part of binding may leave the atoms which are to undergo changes of bonding in an unfavourable position, which is corrected by an interaction of minor importance in the total free energy of binding.

REFERENCE

Witzel, H. (1964). Abstr. 1st. Meeting Federation of European Biochemical Societies, p. 24. London.

The Enzymic Reactivation of Reduced Ribonuclease

P. Venetianer, E.-G. Krause and F. B. Straub

Institute of Medical Chemistry, University of Medicine, Budapest, Hungary

White (1961) and Anfinsen and Haber (1961) described the full reappearance of enzymic activity when reduced ribonuclease was exposed in dilute solution to atmospheric oxygen. We have studied this reaction from the viewpoint of protein biosynthesis, as it appeared to be a suitable *in vitro* model for the formation of the secondary and tertiary structure of newly synthesized ribonuclease. We found in the pancreas of various animal species an enzyme which catalysed this reactivation reaction (Venetianer and Straub, 1963a) and we purified it about a 100-fold. Independently, Goldberger *et al.* (1963) described a similar, and probably identical, enzyme present in rat liver. Both enzymes exert their activity only in the presence of a heat-stable factor which occurs in the protein-free extracts of various animal tissues and yeast. The nature of this heat-stable factor was not clear for some time, yet it is obvious that it plays an important role in the mechanism of action of the ribonuclease-reactivating enzyme.

We have recently found that dehydroascorbic acid can replace the heat-stable factor in the enzymic reactivation of reduced ribonuclease (Venetianer and Straub, 1963b). Ascorbic acid may also be used, but in this case a lag period is observed in the kinetics of the enzymically catalysed reactivation. As a next step we attempted to establish whether this same redox system was responsible for the activity of protein-free tissue extracts in the enzymic reactivation of ribonuclease. It was found that the cofactor-activity of the perchloric acid extracts of various animal tissues was proportional to their ascorbate plus dehydroascorbate content. Extracts of beef adrenal glands exhibited the highest activity. Such extracts were subjected to chromatography on Dowex-1 columns, using a formic acid elution gradient. The activity of effluent fractions was determined in the reactivation test. Maximum cofactor activity was found to be associated with the chemically determined peaks of ascorbate and dehydroascorbate. If the chromatography was carried out in the presence of 0.01 M borate, the peak of dehydroascorbate was shifted, and the corresponding peak of activity was shifted the same way. This evidence strongly suggests that dehydroascorbate is the active factor in the extracts. The quantitative evaluation of these results is somewhat difficult, owing to the rapid decomposition of dehydroascorbate in neutral solutions, and to the presence of factors in tissue extracts which may prevent this decomposition. In spite of the ambiguity introduced by these factors, it may be concluded that dehydroascorbate and ascorbate are together responsible for at least 70% of the cofactor-activity of the extracts.

By the use of pure dehydroascorbate, the role of this substance in the reactivation reaction was studied. In the absence of enzyme, only a minimal amount (less than 5%) of reduced ribonuclease is reactivated by dehydroascorbate alone. However, if the same reaction is carried out in a spectrophotometer cell, a rapid increase in the ultraviolet absorption can be observed with a maximum at 250 mμ. This rise is due to the ascorbic acid formed

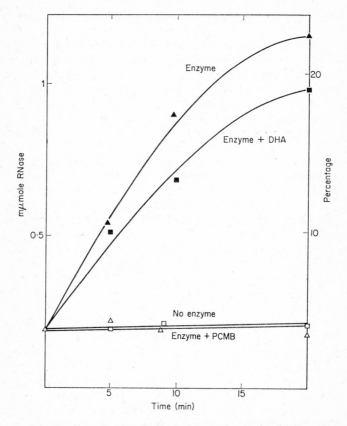

FIGURE 1. Reactivation of reduced ribonuclease, after preincubation with dehydroascorbic acid. *Preincubation.* Reduced ribonuclease (0·1 μmole) + EDTA (15 μmoles) + dehydroascorbic acid (2 μmoles) + pH 7·5 tris-HCl buffer (200 μmoles) were shaken aerobically at 37° for 7 min in a final volume of 2 ml. The mixture was then acidified to pH 3·5 by acetic acid and put on a 220 × 20 mm Sephadex G-25 column. After elution with 0·01 M acetic acid the protein of the front peak was collected. *Incubation mixture.* 5 × 10⁻⁹ moles of the oxidized ribonuclease (inactive) + 10 μmoles EDTA + 120 μmoles pH 7·5 tris-HCl buffer + additions as noted on the curves, were shaken aerobically at 37°C in a final volume of 1·2 ml. □, No addition; ▲, + 50 μg purified reactivating enzyme; ■, + 50 μg purified reactivating enzyme + 1 μmole dehydroascorbic acid (DHA); △, + 50 μg purified reactivating enzyme + 0·08 μmole *p*-chloromercuribenzoate. Ribonuclease activity is expressed as the percentage of the maximal activity of the ribonuclease present in the incubation mixture, and in absolute amounts of active ribonuclease.

during the oxidation of reduced ribonuclease. The quantitative evaluation of this experiment revealed that more than 90% of the SH-groups of the reduced ribonuclease were oxidized by a threefold molar excess of dehydro-ascorbate within 5 min. The addition of the reactivating enzyme did not influence the rate and extent of this reaction. The SH-groups of the reduced ribonuclease are thus rapidly oxidized by dehydroascorbate, without appreciable reactivation. Reactivation of ribonuclease occurred only in the presence of the reactivating enzyme and dehydroascorbic acid. This observation led us to try to separate the oxidation and reactivation reactions.

Fully reduced ribonuclease was incubated with a 2·5-fold excess of dehydro-ascorbate for 7 min, at pH 7·5. Then we separated the low-molecular substances from ribonuclease by means of gel-filtration. The protein was still practically inactive, although its content of free SH-groups was now found to be less than 0·5 SH-group/mole. As Figure 1 demonstrates, the reactivating enzyme was able to activate this ribonuclease without the addition of any co-factor. Dehydroascorbate was if anything an inhibitor of this reaction. Arsenite (10^{-5} M), which was found to be a strong inhibitor of the enzymic reactivation of reduced ribonuclease, did not influence the activation of the dehydroascorbate-oxidized molecule. p-Chloromercuribenzoate inhibited both processes.

These experimental results clearly indicate that the reactivating enzyme is not an oxidoreductase as it was believed to be earlier. The oxidizing agent, dehydroascorbic acid, acts non-enzymically. This leads most probably to the formation of a mixture of randomly oxidized inactive isomers of ribonuclease. The function of the enzyme may be the catalysis of the rearrangement of the disulphide bridges, by lowering the activation energy of the interchange reaction. This explanation is in accordance with the claim that the native structure is the most probable of all possible isomers. In the biosynthetic process the enzyme may act either on the newly formed and fully reduced polypeptide chain, or it may re-arrange any false disulphides which had been formed during the growth of the chain.

REFERENCES

Anfinsen, C. B. and Haber, E. (1961). *J. biol. Chem.* **236**, 1361.
Goldberger, R. F., Epstein, C. J. and Anfinsen, C. B. (1963). *J. biol. Chem.* **238**, 628.
Venetianer, P. and Straub, F. B. (1963a). *Biochim. biophys. Acta* **67**, 166.
Venetianer, P. and Straub, F. B. (1963b). *Acta physiol. Hung.* **24**, 41.
White, F. H., Jr. (1961). *J. biol. Chem.* **236**, 1353.

CHYMOTRYPSIN

On the Structure of Chymotrypsinogen A

B. Keil and F. Šorm

Institute of Organic Chemistry and Biochemistry,
Czechoslovak Academy of Sciences, Prague, Czechoslovakia

As is apparent from the programme of this symposium, our knowledge of organic molecules with a structure fixed by covalent bonds has definitely surpassed the limit of the molecular weight of 20,000.

When, several years ago in Prague, we decided to study the primary structure of chymotrypsinogen and trypsinogen from beef pancreas, it was because of the then existing general trends governing the fields of activities in protein research. It was evident that it would hardly be possible to elucidate the common regularities of protein structure solely by studying one structure. A comparative study of structures with the same function in different organisms, and of those with different functions but produced by the same cells, was therefore undertaken in many laboratories. The work of Tuppy on the structures of cytochrome *c* showed very soon that proteins that perform the same function in different organisms are similar in the part of the molecule essential for their function. Further work in this respect, namely the study of haemoglobins, myoglobins, insulins and tobacco mosaic viruses, furnished information of primary importance for the concepts of protein synthesis, of genetic information, etc.

We were interested in other kinds of comparative study, those leading to knowledge of the structural relations between proteins produced by the same organ, but exerting a distinctly different function. Examples of such proteins were the pancreatic zymogens chymotrypsinogen and trypsinogen. The first approach by means of the comparison of small fragments (Šorm *et al.*, 1958, 1961) was interesting and intriguing, but we soon found that such a study would be relevant only when large defined structures were compared.

We should add that we somewhat over-estimated our capabilities when we started to elucidate simultaneously in the same laboratory the full structures of two proteins with a molecular weight of about 23,000, but we were optimistic because we knew that parallel work was being undertaken on chymotrypsinogen by Hartley and Desnuelle and on trypsinogen by Neurath.

During the short history of research into the primary structure of proteins, it has become evident that parallel studies by independent groups using independent methods have been a great help in the elimination of minor mistakes, which can always be made in the course of such an extensive work.

We hoped to compare and discuss the structure of chymotrypsinogen at the Sixth International Congress of Biochemistry in New York later this year, and we organized our work to that end. However, we accepted with great pleasure the invitation to make the first comparison of results at this Symposium. The advantage of comparing two proposals for a structure is achieved only when entirely independent and complete results are opposed. Here we present our own work without deductions and without using data published by others which had not been checked in our laboratory. Let us hope that, after a discussion of all the results presented at this Symposium, and with additional results from experiments being undertaken in the laboratory, the file on chymotrypsinogen A, independently checked, will be definitely closed, and that within the first half of this year.

Allow me now to summarize the methods and results of our study on the structure of chymotrypsinogen A and to make a short comparison of it with that of trypsinogen (Vaneček *et al.*, 1960; Keil *et al.*, 1962, 1963; Meloun *et al.*, 1963; Kostka *et al.*, 1963; Kluh *et al.*, 1964).

The first enzymic cleavage of chymotrypsinogen A was performed by pepsin (Figure 1). We did not succeed in isolating all fragments of this hydrolysate because of the complexity of the mixture. This hydrolysate is designated in the following figures as P. In another experiment, the peptic hydrolysate was used as starting material for the study of the disulphide bridges. We followed practically the same route as that taken in the case of ribonuclease. The disulphide bridge-containing peptides were isolated in two independent experiments. In one case pepsin cleavage alone was used, whereas in the other case the pepsin digest was digested further by chymotrypsin and trypsin. Fragments containing both cystine and tryptophan were stabilized by converting the cystine residue into two alanine residues by means of Raney-nickel and then hydrogenated in order to convert tryptophan to the octahydro derivative.

The molecule of chymotrypsinogen A is not an ideal structure for tryptic cleavage since the lysine residues are unevenly distributed along the polypeptide chain. One segment of 15 residues contains six lysines and elsewhere there are two sequences containing dilysine. Bearing in mind that there are only four residues of arginine, we find larger structures, longer than the insulin B-chain, which are not accessible to tryptic cleavage. Such peptides are scarcely soluble, and we therefore undertook an additional peptic cleavage of this material, designed in the following schemes as TP-peptides.

The chymotryptic cleavage of *S*-carboxymethyl-chymotrypsinogen was undertaken. The specificity of hydrolysis was increased by adding trypsin inhibitor to the chymotrypsin. The peptides isolated during this study represented approximately two-thirds of the whole molecule, and excluded those containing one of the two histidines present in the molecule and those peptides containing methionine.

We have proceeded by using the method introduced by Hoang *et al.* (1963) for the separation of the three chains of chymotrypsin in a pure state. This technique gives access on a preparative scale to the chains with molecular weights less than one half that of the parent molecule. The C-chain was digested with chymotrypsin. The amino acid distribution within the B-chain did not, on the other hand, allow this approach to be used to obtain data

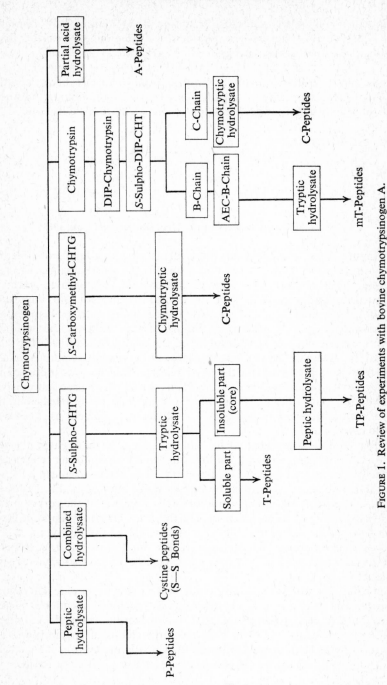

FIGURE 1. Review of experiments with bovine chymotrypsinogen A.

additional to our previous results. Therefore B. Meloun in our laboratory has modified the S-sulphocysteine residues by ethylenimine, converting them into the S-(β-aminoethyl)cysteine derivatives (Figure 2). Following this procedure, first described by Raftery and Cole (1963), the sites of modified cysteines are accessible to hydrolysis with trypsin. In the case of the work on the B-chain the specificity of trypsin was increased by inhibiting the traces of chymotryptic activity with N-tosylphenylalanylchloromethylketone.

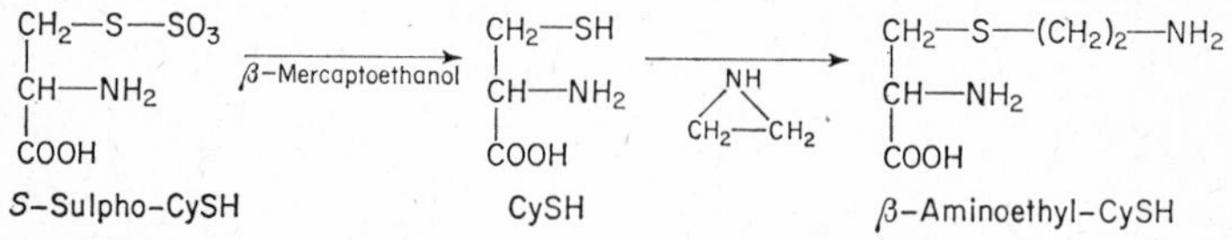

FIGURE 2. Substitution of cysteine residues (Raftery and Cole, 1963).

In Figure 3, the first part of the molecule is shown. It represents the first 145 residues, or in terms of chymotrypsin, the A- and B-chains. The two dipeptides released during the activation of chymotrypsinogen are enclosed by dotted lines. It is apparent from this scheme that in most cases the results are sufficiently unambiguous to provide the necessary overlaps between the various fragments. At the very beginning of the chain, in the so-called A-peptide, we have not as yet established the complete sequence. The sites marked by zigzag lines are lacking overlaps. For comparative purposes these three fragments are placed in the same relative order as was proposed by Hartley,[†] but this arrangement of the fragments is still open to independent confirmation. The three peptides, which we have so far isolated after the above mentioned aminoethylcysteine modification, helped us to derive additional overlaps.

In Figure 4, the second half of the molecule, the C-chain of chymotrypsin, is shown. Here again, an additional overlap is necessary in order to establish the relative positions of two of the fragments. The peptides indicated by mT again illustrate specific cleavages by trypsin at the sites of modified cysteine residues. There have been many studies of the sequence at the carboxyl end of chymotrypsin. Experiments involving the use of carboxypeptidase have given rise to four different results. We are presenting the fifth version, and we hope that we are on the safe side because our C-terminal fragment was isolated and analysed as an individual peptide from the chymotryptic cleavage.

The relative positions of the disulphide bridges (Figure 5) were determined independently in two series of experiments as previously mentioned. There were parallel studies by Hartley that gave the same result. Although five bridges exist in the molecule, only two hold the three chains of chymotrypsin together. The two histidine residues, one of which is involved in the enzymic activity (marked on Figure 5 by an asterisk), are brought close together by

† B. S. Hartley: "The Structure and Activity of Chymotrypsin". See p. 47.

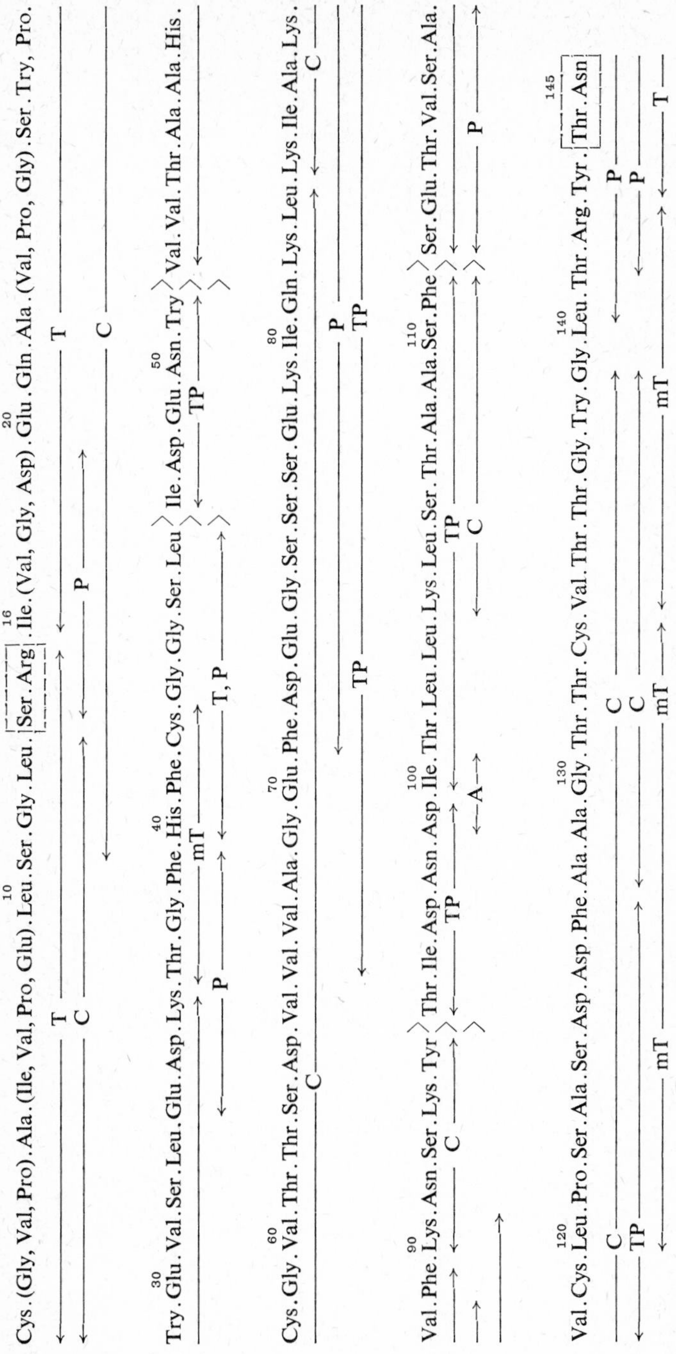

Cys.(Gly, Val, Pro).Ala.(Ile, Val, Pro, Glu).Leu.Ser.Gly.Leu.Ser.Arg.Ile.(Val, Gly, Asp).Glu.Gln.Ala.(Val, Pro, Gly).Ser.Try, Pro.
10 16 20
T C T P C
Try.Glu.Val.Ser.Leu.Glu.Asp.Lys.Thr.Gly.Phe.His.Phe.Cys.Gly.Gly.Ser.Leu Ile.Asp.Glu.Asn.Try Val.Val.Thr.Ala.Ala.His.
30 40 50
mT TP P T, P
Cys.Gly.Val.Thr.Thr.Ser.Asp.Val.Val.Val.Ala.Gly.Glu.Phe.Asp.Glu.Gly.Ser.Ser.Ser.Glu.Lys.Ile.Gln.Lys.Leu.Lys.Ile.Ala.Lys.
60 70 80
C C P TP TP
Val.Phe.Lys.Asn.Ser.Lys.Tyr Thr.Ile.Asp.Asn.Asp.Ile.Thr.Leu.Leu.Lys.Leu.Ser.Thr.Ala.Ala.Ser.Phe Ser.Glu.Thr.Val.Ser.Ala.
90 100 110
C TP TP A C P
Val.Cys.Leu.Pro.Ser.Ala.Ser.Asp.Asp.Phe.Ala.Ala.Gly.Thr.Thr.Cys.Val.Thr.Thr.Gly.Try.Gly.Leu.Thr.Arg.Tyr.Thr.Asn
120 130 140 145
C C P TP C P mT mT mT T

FIGURE 3. Chymotrypsinogen—residues 1–145.

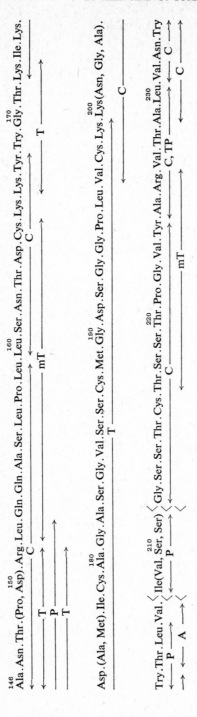

FIGURE 4. Chymotrypsinogen—residues 146–241.

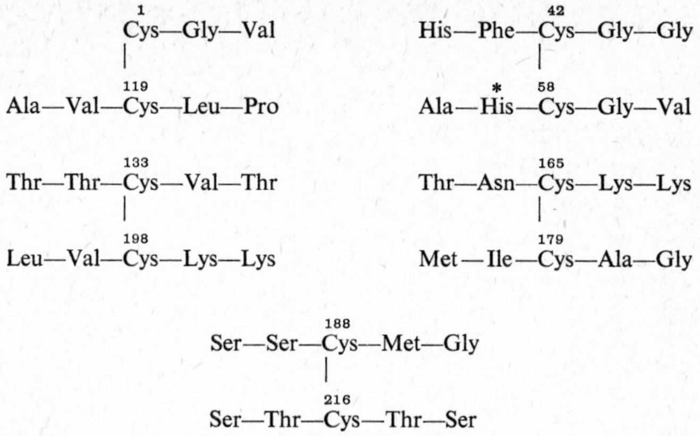

```
    1
  Cys—Gly—Val                  His—Phe—Cys—Gly—Gly
   |                                    |
   119                                * 58
Ala—Val—Cys—Leu—Pro             Ala—His—Cys—Gly—Val

   133                                  165
Thr—Thr—Cys—Val—Thr             Thr—Asn—Cys—Lys—Lys
   |                                    |
   198                                  179
Leu—Val—Cys—Lys—Lys             Met—Ile—Cys—Ala—Gly


                        188
              Ser—Ser—Cys—Met—Gly
                        |
                        216
              Ser—Thr—Cys—Thr—Ser
```

FIGURE 5. The disulphide bonds of chymotrypsinogen.

TABLE I. Number of Residues in Chymotrypsinogen

Amino acid	Analytical data†	Found in peptides	Difference
Arg	4	4	
His	2	2	
Lys	14	14	
Glu	15	15	
Asp	22	22	
Ser	29	28	− 1
Thr	22	23	+ 1
Tyr	4	4	
Phe	6	6	
Try	7	7	
Cys/2	10	10	
Met	2	2	
Ala	22	22	
Gly	22	22	
Ile	10	10	
Leu	19	18	− 1
Pro	9	9	
Val	22	23	+ 1
Total	241	241	

† Zmrahl (1962).

.Pro.Leu.Leu.Ser.Asn.Thr.Asp.Cys.Lys.

.Ala.Gly.Thr.Thr.Cys.Val.

.Met.Ile.Cys.Ala.Gly.Ala.Ser.Gly.Val.Ser.Cys.Met.Gly.Asp.Ser.Gly.Gly.Pro.Leu.Val.Cys.Lys.Lys.
                         *

.Gly.Ser.Ser.Thr.Cys.Thr.Ser.Thr.Pro.Gly.Val.Tyr.Ala.Arg.Val.

Chymotrypsinogen A

.Pro.Ile.Leu.Ser.Asp.Ser.Ser.Cys.Lys.

.Ala(Gly, Thr, Glu)Cys.Leu.

.Met.Phe.Cys.Ala.Gly.Tyr.Leu.Glu.Gly.Gly.Lys.Asn.Ser.Cys.Gln.Gly.Gly.Asp.Ser.Gly.Pro.Val.Val.Cys.Ser.Gly.Lys.
               *

.Gly.Ser.Gly.Cys.Ala.Gln.Lys.Asn.Lys.Pro.Gly.Val.Tyr.Thr.Lys.Val.

Trypsinogen

.His.Phe.Cys.Gly.Gly.Ser.Leu.

.Val.Thr.Ala.Ala.His.Cys.
    *

Chymotrypsinogen A

.His.Phe.Cys(Gly, Gly, Ser, Leu).

.Val.Ser.Ala.Ala.His.Cys.

Trypsinogen

FIGURE 6. Comparison of chymotrypsinogen A and trypsinogen.

one of the disulphide bridges of the B-chain. The position of this active histidine has been determined by Meloun and Pospíšilová (1964).

In Table I a comparison is made of the number of amino acid residues found in peptide fragments with the quantitative amino acid analysis of the parent protein made in our laboratory by Zmrhal (1962). The difference still involves one residue each of serine, threonine, leucine and valine.

Finally, I would like to come back to the original proposition, that of the similarity or difference between chymotrypsinogen A and trypsinogen.

It was exactly 10 years ago that we isolated two tripeptides containing arginine, and two containing histidine, from chymotrypsinogen and trypsinogen respectively, which we found to be of similar sequence. It was certainly not very wise of us, knowing only those four tripeptides, to have predicted then that perhaps chymotrypsinogen and trypsinogen were built in a similar manner.

Admittedly it became more and more surprising to us during the work on the complete structures of both proteins that this original hypothesis was not so exaggerated. Although the primary structure of trypsinogen is not as yet available in complete form, large fragments have been characterized in our laboratory by the group of Mikeš et al. (1964) and so we can now compare them. It was known several years ago that the segments containing the active serine residue were very similar. This similarity can now be extended to large parts of the molecule. Figure 6 illustrates two of the most striking examples, although it would be possible to discuss additional similarities in other parts of the two proteins. The identity of amino acids residues in corresponding segments of the two molecules is complemented by the occurrence of very similar residues (like leucine for isoleucine, arginine for lysine, serine for threonine), so that the overall structures of the two polypeptide chains suggest a common building scheme.

The examples shown in Figure 6 represent roughly 30% of the whole molecules. This shows clearly that not only some active sites, but also large segments of the primary structures including disulphide bridges, and consequently the three dimensional configurations are similar.

REFERENCES

Dinh van Hoang, Rovery, M., Guidoni, A. and Desnuelle, P. (1963). *Biochim. biophys. Acta* 69, 188.

Keil, B., Prusík, Z. and Šorm, F. (1963). *Biochim. biophys. Acta* 78, 559.

Keil, B., Šorm, F., Meloun, B., Vaněček, J., Kostka, V. and Prusík, Z. (1962). *Biochim. biophys. Acta* 56, 595.

Kluh, I., Junge, J., Morávek, L., Meloun, B. and Šorm, F. (1964). Abstracts, VIth Internat. Congress of Biochemistry (New York).

Kostka, V., Meloun, B. and Šorm, F. (1963). *Coll. Czech. Chem. Commun.* 28, 2753.

Meloun, B. and Pospíšilová, D. (1964). *Biochim. biophys. Acta* (in press).

Meloun, B., Kostka, V., Keil, B. and Šorm, F. (1963). *Coll. Czech. Chem. Commun.* 28, 2749.

Mikeš, O., Holeyšovsky, V., Tomášek, V. and Šorm, F. (1964). Abstracts, VIth Internat. Congress of Biochemistry, New York.

Raftery, M. A. and Cole, R. D. (1963). *Biochem. biophys. Res. Commun.* **10**, 467.

Šorm, F., Keil, B., Holeyšovský, V., Meloun, B., Mikeš, O. and Vaněček, J. (1958). *Coll. Czech. Chem. Commun.* **23**, 985.

Šorm, F., Keil, B., Vaněček, J., Tomášek, V., Mikeš, O., Meloun, B., Kostka, V. and Holeyšovský, V. (1961). *Coll. Czech. Chem. Commun.* **26**, 531.

Vaněček, J., Meloun, B., Kostka, V., Keil, B. and Šorm, F. (1960). *Biochim. biophys. Acta* **37**, 169.

Zmrhal, Z. (1962). *Coll. Czech. Chem. Commun.* **27**, 2934.

The Structure and Activity of Chymotrypsin

B. S. Hartley

*Medical Research Council Laboratory of Molecular Biology,
Cambridge, England†*

The amino acid sequence shown in Figure 4 represents the conclusions from my six-year study of bovine chymotrypsinogen-A. I believe it to be correct, but will re-examine any remaining areas of disagreement which Dr. Keil may have mentioned in his accompanying paper (p. 37). As I have summarized the evidence for this sequence elsewhere (Hartley, 1964), I will confine my discussion of the structure to a brief description of the isolation of the tryptic peptides from the B- and C-chains of α-chymotrypsin. The performic oxidized or S-sulpho chains (Hartley, 1962) are always heterogeneous, and the best preparations of the chains were made by reducing di-isopropyl-phosphoryl-α-chymotrypsin with β-mercaptoethanol in 8 M urea, removing

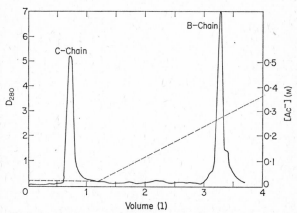

FIGURE 1. Separation of the B- and C-chains of S-carboxymethyl DIP-α-chymotrypsin on a DEAE-cellulose column, with a linear gradient of 0·02–0·50 M tris-acetate, 8 M urea, pH 8·0.

† The early stages of this work were carried out in the Department of Biochemistry, University of Washington, Seattle, U.S.A., in collaboration with Miss Dorothy Kauffman and Professor Hans Neurath, and in the Department of Biochemistry, University of Cambridge. I should like to thank Mrs B. Pickles, Mr. A. Weeds and particularly Mr. A. Seeley for their assistance in the many experiments which were involved, and all my colleagues in the Protein Chemistry Divison of the Laboratory of Molecular Biology for their invaluable advice.

TABLE I. Tryptic Peptides from the Carboxymethyl B-Chain

	T2	T3	T4	T5	T6	T7	T8	T9	T10	C-terminus	Whole chain
Lys	1·0(1)	1·0(1)	1·0(1)	1·0(1)	1·0(1)	1·0(1)	1·0(1)	1·0(1)	—	—	8·0(8)
His	—	2·0(2)	—	—	—	—	—	—	—	—	2·0(2)
Arg	—	—	—	—	—	—	—	—	1·0(1)	—	1·0(1)
CM-Cys	—	1·7(2)	—	—	—	—	—	—	1·7(2)	—	3·9‡(4)
Asp	2·0(2)	3·8(4)	—	—	—	—	1·0(1)	4·0(4)	2·0(2)	—	12·2(13)
Thr	0·1	3·7(4)	—	—	—	—	—	1·9(2)	6·4(7)	—	11·1(13)
Ser	1·8(2)	4·3(5)	—	—	—	—	0·7(1)	1·1(1)	5·2(6)	—	12·4(15)
Glu	3·8(4)	4·1(4)	1·0(1)	—	—	—	—	—	1·1(1)	—	10·0(10)
Pro	2·0(2)	—	—	—	—	—	—	—	1·0(1)	—	3·0(3)
Gly	2·0(2)	5·2(6)	—	—	1·0(1)	—	—	—	3·0(3)	—	11·4(11)
Ala	1·0(1)	3·1(3)	—	—	—	—	—	—	6·0(6)	—	10·6(11)
Val	2·3(3)	4·0(6)	—	—	—	1·0(1)	—	—	3·0(3)	—	11·4(13)
Met	—	—	—	—	—	—	—	—	—	—	—
Ile	0·3(1)	0·9(1)	1·0(1)	—	1·0(1)	—	—	1·8(2)	—	—	6·0(6)
Leu	1·0(1)	1·0(1)	—	1·0(1)	—	—	—	2·8(3)	2·8(3)	—	9·1(9)
Tyr	—	—	—	—	—	—	—	0·9(1)	—	+ (1)	1·6(2)
Phe	—	3·0(3)	—	—	—	1·0(1)	—	—	2·0(2)	—	6·0(6)
Try†	2·1(2)	1·2(1)	—	—	—	—	—	—	1·1(1)	—	4·1(4)
Total	21	43	3	2	3	3	3	14	38	1	131

† From spectrum.   ‡ As CySO₃H.

The ratios shown are based on the mean of several quantitative analyses of 18 hr acid hydrolysates, uncorrected for destruction or incomplete hydrolysis. In the whole B-chain the cystine is estimated after performic oxidation as cysteic acid. Tryptophan is estimated from the absorption spectrum. The figures in brackets give the residues indicated by sequence studies.

TABLE II. Tryptic Peptides from the Carboxymethyl C-Chain

	T11A	T12	T14A	T15	T16	T17	T18	Whole C-chain
Lys	—	1·0 (1)	2·0 (2)	1·0 (1)	1·0 (1)	(1)	—	6·1 (6)
His	—	—	—	—	—	—	—	—
Arg	1·0 (1)	0·7 (1)	—	—	—	(1)	—	2·1 (2)
CM.Cys	2·0 (2)	2·0 (2)	—	—	2·8‡ (3)	(1)	—	4·5 (5)
Asp	0·9 (1)	0·9 (1)	—	—	2·0 (2)	(1)	(2)	9·0 (9)
Thr	—	1·9 (2)	0·8 (1)	—	—	(4)	(2)	8·8 (9)
Ser	—	2·0 (2)	—	—	3·8 (4)	(6)	—	9·7 (12)
Glu	1·0 (1)	1·0 (1)	—	—	—	—	(2)	4·2 (4)
Pro	1·0 (1)	—	1·0 (1)	—	1·1 (1)	(1)	—	4·2 (4)
Gly	—	0·9 (1)	—	—	5·3 (5)	(4)	—	9·9 (10)
Ala	—	—	—	—	3·0 (3)	(2)	(3)	9·9 (10)
Val	—	—	—	—	1·7 (2)	(3)	(3)	7·2 (8)
Met	—	—	—	—	2·0 (2)	—	—	1·8 (2)
Ile	—	3·9 (4)	—	0·9 (1)	0·8 (1)	(1)	—	2·4 (3)
Leu	—	—	—	—	1·0 (1)	(1)	(2)	8·1 (8)
Tyr	—	—	0·6 (1)	—	—	(1)	—	1·8 (2)
Phe	—	—	—	—	—	—	—	—
Try†	—	—	+ (1)	—	—	(2)	(1)	3·7 (4)
Total	6	15	6	2	25	29	15	98

† From spectrum. ‡ As $CySO_3H$.
Analyses as Table I. T17 and T18 form part of the "core" and were not purified.

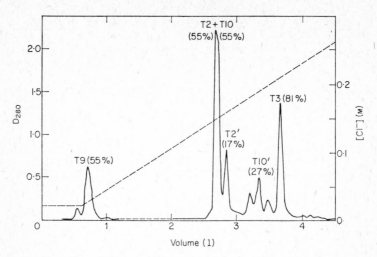

FIGURE 2. Separation of the tryptic "B-core" on a DEAE-cellulose column, with a linear gradient of 0·02–0·22 M tris-chloride, 8 M urea, pH 8·0. The indicated yields of the tryptic peptides shown in Table II were calculated after further purification on Sephadex G–25.

excess thiol on Sephadex G–25, coupling with iodoacetate and separating the chains in 8 M urea on DEAE-cellulose (Figure 2).

Tryptic digests of the B-chain give soluble peptides T4–T8 plus free tyrosine (Table I) and a "core" insoluble at pH 4. This "core" separates in 8 M urea solutions on DEAE-cellulose to give mainly T2, T3, T9 and T10 (Figure 2) which were further purified on Sephadex G–25. The minor products T2′ (residues 16–29) and T10′ (residues 108–141) are probably due to traces of chymotrypsin in the digest. The amino acid composition of these peptides, determined by analysis and from sequence studies, are compared in Table I with that of the whole B-chain. The evidence for their sequence and arrangement has been summarized elsewhere (Hartley, 1964).

The story of the tryptic digests of the C-chain is less tidy. The soluble peptides T11A–T16 (Table II) are easily purified on paper, but the remaining C-core, a mixture of T16, T17 and T18, is particularly insoluble, even in 8 M urea or 30% acetic acid, and does not lend itself to fractional extraction techniques. However, prolonged chymotryptic digestion of this "core" gives the peptides shown in Figure 3, and the insoluble residue can be dissolved in 98% formic acid and diluted directly into aqueous pepsin to give peptides P1 and P2 (Figure 3). Alternative papain or subtilisin digests of the C-core allowed us to derive its sequence (Hartley, 1964).

We also reinvestigated the sequence of the oxidized A-chain and detected errors in the sequence reported by Meedom (1958). Here, as in all recent sequence work, the sequential "Dansyl-Edman" technique developed by Mr. W. R. Gray proved of great value, giving reliable results with as little as 0·02 μ moles of a penta- or hexapeptide (Gray and Hartley, 1963).

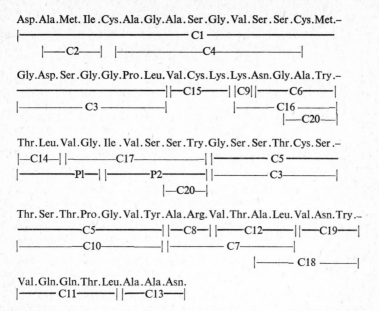

FIGURE 3. Chymotryptic and peptic peptides from the C-core. Major products are denoted by heavy lines and minor products by light lines. C indicates chymotryptic peptides and P indicates peptic peptides.

Determination of the five disulphide bridges by a "diagonal" paper technique proved unexpectedly easy (Brown and Hartley, 1963). The bridges shown in Figure 4 agree with those published independently by Keil, Prusík and Šorm (1963). Bridge 1–122 connects the A- and B-chains, and bridge 136–201 joins the B- and C-chains. The important "histidine loop" formed by bridge 42–58 occurs one third of the way down the B-chain and a "knot" of bridges 182–168, 191–221, and 201–136 surrounds the active Ser-195 of the C-chain.

It is now appropriate to re-examine our knowledge of the activation of chymotrypsinogen and the mechanism of action of the enzyme. Much of the evidence for the following opinions has been reviewed previously (e.g. Neurath and Hartley, 1959; Hartley, 1960; Desnuelle and Rovery, 1961; Neurath, 1964), so I will generally give references only to more recent papers.

ACTIVATION OF CHYMOTRYPSINOGEN-A

This occurs when the bond between Arg-15 and Ile-16 is split by trypsin to give π-chymotrypsin. Changes in optical rotation or absorption spectra indicate that there is an accompanying alteration of tertiary structure, but this may be relatively minor since acylation or guanidation of all the free amino groups of the zymogen neither prevents the activation nor affects the activity of the resulting substituted enzyme (Chervenka and Wilcox, 1956).

Cys.Gly.Val.Pro.Ala. Ile .Gln.Pro.Val.Leu. Ser .Gly.Leu.--- Ser .Arg.--- Ile. Val.
1   2   3   4   5   6   7   8   9   10   11   12   13   14   15   16   17
←————————————————————— T1 ——————————————————→ ←——————

Gly.Asp.Glu.Glu.Ala. Val.Pro.Gly. Ser .Try.Pro.Try.Gln. Val. Ser .Leu.Gln.Asp.Lys.
18   19   20   21   22   23   24   25   26   27   28   29   30   31   32   33   34   35   36
——————————————————————————— T2 ——————————————————————————→

Thr.Gly.Phe.HIS.Phe.Cys.Gly.Gly. Ser .Leu. Ile .Asn.Glu.Asn.Try. Val. Val.Thr.Ala.
37   38   39   40   41   42   43   44   45   46   47   48   49   50   51   52   53   54   55
←——

Ala.HIS.Cys.Gly. Val.Thr.Thr. Ser .Asp.Val. Val. Val.Ala.Gly.Glu.Phe.Asp.Gln.Gly.
56   57   58   59   60   61   62   63   64   65   66   67   68   69   70   71   72   73   74
————————————— T3 ———

Ser . Ser . Ser .Glu.Lys. Ile .Gln.Lys.Leu.Lys. Ile .Ala.Lys. Val.Phe.Lys.Asn. Ser .Lys.
75   76   77   78   79   80   81   82   83   84   85   86   87   88   89   90   91   92   93
————————————————————→←— T4 —→ ← T5 → ←— T6 —→ ←— T7 —→ ←— T8 —→

Tyr.Asn. Ser .Leu.Thr. Ile .Asn.Asn.Asn. Ile .Thr.Leu.Leu.Lys.Leu. Ser .Thr.Ala.Ala.
94   95   96   97   98   99   100 101 102 103 104 105 106 107 108 109 110 111 112
←————————————————————— T9 ——————————————————————→←————

Ser .Phe. Ser .Gln.Thr. Val. Ser .Ala. Val.Cys.Leu.Pro. Ser .Ala. Ser .Asp.Asp.Phe.Ala.
113 114 115 116 117 118 119 120 121 122 123 124 125 126 127 128 129 130 131
——— T10 —————————

Ala.Gly.Thr.Thr.Cys. Val.Thr.Thr.Gly.Try.Gly.Leu.Thr.Arg.Tyr.---Thr.Asn.----
132 133 134 135 136 137 138 139 140 141 142 143 144 145 146   147 148
——→

Ala.Asn.Thr.Pro.Asp.Arg.Leu.Gln.Gln.Ala. Ser .Leu.Pro.Leu.Leu. Ser .Asn.Thr.Asn.
149 150 151 152 153 154 155 156 157 158 159 160 161 162 163 164 165 166 167
←——————— T11A ——————→←————————————————————T12——————————————

Cys.Lys.Lys.Tyr.Try.Gly.Thr.Lys. Ile .Lys.Asp.Ala.Met. Ile .Cys.Ala.Gly.Ala. Ser .
168 169 170 171 172 173 174 175 176 177 178 179 180 181 182 183 184 185 186
————————→←——————— T14A ——————————→←— T15 →←———

Gly. Val. Ser . Ser .Cys.Met.Gly.Asp. Ser .Gly.Gly.Pro.Leu. Val.Cys.Lys.Lys.Asn.Gly.
187 188 189 190 191 192 193 194 195 196 197 198 199 200 201 202 203 204 205
————————————T16——————————————————————————————————————→←——

Ala.Try.Thr.Leu. Val.Gly. Ile . Val. Ser . Ser .Try.Gly. Ser . Ser .Thr.Cys. Ser .Thr. Ser .
206 207 208 209 210 211 212 213 214 215 216 217 218 219 220 221 222 223 224
————————————————————————————————————— T17 ————————————

Thr.Pro.Gly. Val.Tyr.Ala.Arg. Val.Thr.Ala.Leu. Val.Asn.Try. Val.Gln.Gln.Thr.Leu.
225 226 227 228 229 230 231 232 233 234 235 236 237 238 239 240 241 242 243
—————————————————→←——————————————————————T18——————————

Ala.Ala.Asn.
244 245 246
—————————→

Disulphide bridges: 1–122; 42–58; 136–201; 168–182; 191–221.

FIGURE 4. Amino acid sequence of bovine chymotrypsinogen-A. The arrows indicate the tryptic peptides shown in Tables I and II. In α-chymotrypsin, the A-chain consists of residues 1–13, the B-chain of residues 16–146 and the C-chain of residues 149–246. Throughout this paper Asn indicates asparagine, Gln—glutamine, Ile—isoleucine and Cys indicates half-cystine, carboxymethyl cysteine or cysteic acid, depending on the context.

One can therefore assume that the substituents do not hinder the configurational change, and that the environment of the amino groups is similar in both chymotrypsinogen and chymotrypsin. Incidentally, this evidence also suggests that electrostatic interactions generally play little part in stabilizing the tertiary structure of this enzyme. Furthermore, there are indications that the substrate-binding site may pre-exist in the zymogen (Vaslow and Doherty, 1953; Neurath, 1964).

π-Chymotrypsin is very susceptible to chymotryptic attack at the Leu-13. Ser-14 bond, liberating Ser.Arg to give δ-chymotrypsin. This bond can also be split by digesting chymotrypsinogen with chymotrypsin, but here an inactive but activatable neo-chymotrypsinogen is formed (Desnuelle and Rovery, 1961). Further chymotryptic splits between Tyr-146 and Thr-147 and between Asn-148 and Ala-149 give α-chymotrypsin, but yield neo-chymotrypsinogens if they precede the tryptic activation. We must conclude that these residues are on the "surface" in both chymotrypsinogen and chymotrypsin. The observation that Ala-149 reacts with fluorodinitrobenzene in native α-chymotrypsin (Massey and Hartley, 1956) and that Tyr-146 specifically iodinates without inactivating the enzyme (Glazer and Sanger, 1963), support this conclusion.

However, the N-terminal isoleucine of the B-chain does not react with fluorodinitrobenzene in native α-chymotrypsin (Massey and Hartley, 1956) and Labouesse, et al.† show that modification of this "buried" group affects the tertiary structure of the enzyme. We conclude that cleavage between Arg-15 and Ile-16 (but not between Leu-13 and Ser-14) removes basic hydrophilic residues and allows the "acidic hydrophobic N-terminus of the B-chain to find its complement elsewhere in the molecule" (Hartley, 1963), causing a limited but crucial change in tertiary structure.

THE MECHANISM OF ACTION OF α-CHYMOTRYPSIN

This can be summarized as follows

$$E\text{—}H + R.CO - X \overset{K_m}{\rightleftarrows} E\text{—}H(R.CO\text{—}X) \quad \ldots \text{(Binding)}$$

$$\overset{k_2}{\rightarrow} E\text{—}CO.R + HX \qquad \ldots \text{(Acylation)}$$

$$\overset{k_3}{\underset{H_2O}{\rightarrow}} E\text{—}H + R.COOH \qquad \ldots \text{(Deacylation)}$$

$$(1)$$

Studies with p-nitrophenyl acetate (R.CO—X in (1)) have shown that acylation of Ser-195, with elimination of a "burst" of nitrophenol (HX in (1)) is an intermediate step in the catalysis, and that both acylation and deacylation appear to require the participation of an unionized imidazole side-chain. The binding step, however, is not greatly influenced by pH over the range pH 5–8.

† B. Labouesse et al.: Characterization of a Residue Controlling the Activity and the Conformation of Chymotrypsin. See p. 71.

TABLE III. Kinetic Constants for Chymotryptic Hydrolysis of *N*-Acetyl L-Amino Acid Esters

	Side chain	K_m (mM)	k (sec^{-1})		Side chain	K_m (mM)	k (sec^{-1})
1	HO—⟨phenyl⟩—CH$_2$—	0·7	193	6	(H$_3$C)$_2$CH—CH$_2$—	3·1	4·4
2	⟨indole⟩—CH$_2$—	0·1	51	7	CH$_3$—CH$_2$—CH$_2$—	10·2	2·7
3	⟨phenyl⟩—CH$_2$—	1·2	53	8	(H$_3$C)$_2$CH—	112	0·15
4	⟨cyclohexyl⟩—CH$_2$—	0·2	14	9	CH$_3$—	611	1·29
5	HO—⟨phenyl⟩—C(CH$_3$)$_2$—	Not hydrolysed		10	H—	96	0·01

At pH 7·9, 25°C. For these substrates, K_m approximates the true dissociation constant and k, the zero order turnover constant, approximates the rate of acylation (k_2 in (1)).

(1) *N*-Acetyl-L-tyrosine ethyl ester and (2) *N*-acetyl-L-tryptophan ethyl ester (Cunningham and Brown, 1956). (3) Acetyl-L-phenylalanine methyl ester and (4) Acetyl-L-*p*-cyclohexylalanine methyl ester (Jones and Niemann, 1963). (5) *N*-Acetyl-*ββ*-dimethyl-L-tyrosine methyl ester (Abrash and Niemann, 1963). (6) Acetyl-L-leucine methyl ester. (7) Acetyl-L-norvaline methyl ester. (8) Acetyl-L-valine methyl ester and (9) Acetyl-L-alanine methyl ester (Jones and Niemann, 1962). (10) Acetylglycine methyl ester (Wolf and Niemann, 1963).

Table III shows kinetic constants for some amino acid ester substrates of chymotrypsin. We see that the best substrates ((1) to (3)) have an aromatic ring as a β-substituent in the side chain. I doubt whether π-bonds play a big part in the binding, since the cyclohexyl derivative (4) binds more strongly than the phenylalanine ester (3) and is split almost as rapidly. However, a β-methylene group in the substrate appears to be an important feature, since the $\beta\beta'$-dimethyltyrosine ester (5) is not attacked, and the valine ester (8) is a much poorer substrate than the leucine (6) and norvaline (7) esters. Such reasoning leads to the concept of the binding site as a "hydrophobic slit" with a narrow "neck" corresponding to the β-methylene of the substrate.

The specificity of chymotrypsin is generally exhibited in the acylation step (k_2) which is rate-limiting with most substrates, but the good leaving group in N-carbobenzoxy-L-tyrosine nitrophenyl ester makes deacylation (k_3) rate-limiting with this substrate, as with the comparable acetyl nitrophenyl ester (NPA) (Gutfreund and Hammond, 1959). Table IV summarizes one of the most revealing features of catalysis by chymotrypsin: with the two substrates shown we are certain that the turnover rate represents the hydrolysis of the acyl-serine in the active centre. The rate of hydrolysis of carbobenzoxy-tyrosyl-O-Ser-195 is 46,000 times faster than that of O-acetyl-Ser-195.

TABLE IV. Hydrolysis of Acyl-Enzyme Intermediates

Acyl group	k_w (sec^{-1})	Relative rate
Carbobenzoxy-tyrosyl-	553	46,000
Acetyl-	0·012	1

k_w is the turnover rate at pH 8·0, 30°C for N-carbobenzoxy-L-tyrosine nitrophenyl ester (Martin, Golubow and Axelrod, 1959) or at pH 8·0, 25°C for p-nitrophenyl acetate (Neurath and Hartley, 1959).

Figure 5 purports to explain this phenomenon. We have suggested that substrate-binding induces a configurational adaptation of the enzyme which brings activating groups into favourable juxtaposition (Neurath and Hartley, 1959; Hartley, 1960). Thus, in Figure 5(a), the aromatic ring of the tyrosyl substrate locks the "histidine loop" into the optimal configuration relative to the acyl-serine bond. With the acetyl-enzyme (Figure 5(b)) no such orientation is possible, but the remarkable effect of indole is easily seen in Figure 5(c). Indole, normally a competitive inhibitor, binds to the acyl-enzyme and increases its rate of hydrolysis (E.S. Awad in Hartley, 1960; Foster, 1961). Similarly, Figure 5(d) explains the effect of indole on the rate of chymotryptic hydrolysis of acyl glycine esters (Applewhite, Martin and Niemann, 1958). The absence of a bulky side chain allows the configurational change; with bigger side chains such as valine, this is not possible (Applewhite and Niemann, 1959).

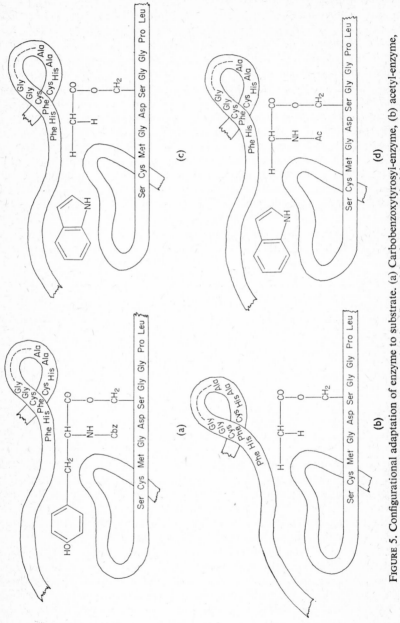

FIGURE 5. Configurational adaptation of enzyme to substrate. (a) Carbobenzoxytyrosyl-enzyme, (b) acetyl-enzyme, (c) acetyl-enzyme + indole, (d) acetylglycyl-enzyme + indole.

CHEMICAL MODIFICATION OF CHYMOTRYPSIN

The modification of chymotrypsin by organophosphorus compounds has illuminated the importance of Ser-195. Koshland, Strumeyer and Ray (1962) have reviewed the evidence from photo-oxidation or dinitrophenylation which points to the participation of a histidine residue in the catalysis, and they also show that specific alkylation of Met-192 with iodoacetate increases K_m but does not affect activity. I will therefore confine myself to some recent studies with "substrate-analogue reagents" which bind at the active centre and there alkylate or acylate adjoining residues. Schoellman and Shaw (1963) showed that tosyl-L-phenylalanyl chloromethane (Figure 6) inhibits chymotrypsin by reacting with a single histidine residue. We have recently identified this residue as His-57 (Smillie and Hartley, 1964). Surprisingly, however, two comparable reagents, 3-phenoxy-1,2-epoxypropane and diphenylcarbamyl chloride (Erlanger and Cohen, 1963), which also inhibit specifically and stoichiometrically, react with Met-192 and Ser-195 respectively (Brown and Hartley, 1964). These residues are all therefore in or near the active centre. The geometry of these reagents must dictate which particular residue they attack, but the degree of free rotation in the reagents used makes any present attempt at steric explanations rather unconvincing.

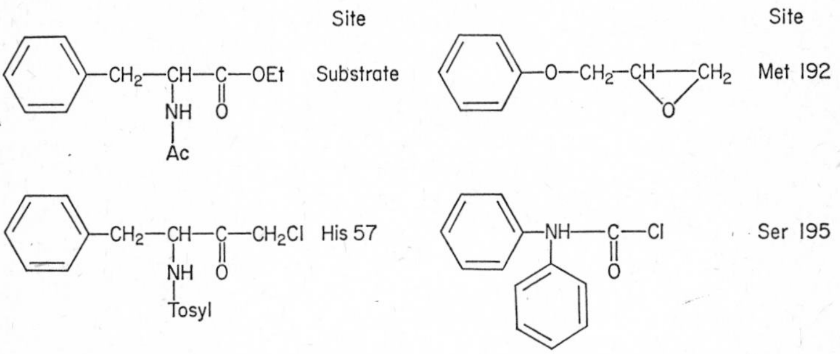

FIGURE 6. Site of reaction of "substrate analogue" reagents (Brown and Hartley, 1964; Smillie and Hartley, 1964).

Figure 7 compares the "serine" and "histidine loop" sequences in bovine trypsin and chymotrypsin-A (Smillie and Hartley, 1964). We also find that the histidine sequences in chymotrypsin-B are the same as those in -A, and have indications that a similar "histidine loop" is found in porcine elastase. This remarkable similarity suggests that these sequences are essential to the active centre of all these "serine enzymes". There is therefore some justification for writing a mechanism of action which involves both histidine residues, as in Figure 8. Here, hydrogen bonding of one imidazole to the serine oxygen encourages attack by the substrate carbonyl group, while the electrons are transferred to a water molecule activated by the second imidazole (Figure

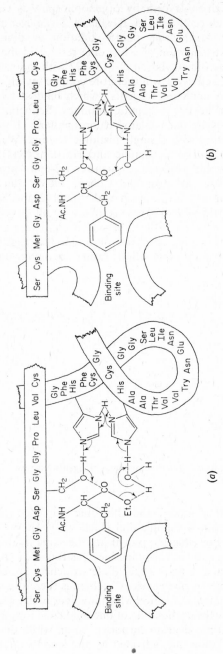

FIGURE 8. Possible mechanism of chymotryptic hydrolysis. (a) Acylation, (b) deacylation.

ACTIVE SERINE SEQUENCES

Chymotrypsin-A

−Ala.Met. Ile .Cys. Ala.Gly.Ala. Ser . Gly.Val. Ser .−

Ser . Cys.Met. Gly.Asp.SER.Gly. Gly. Pro .Leu. Val .Cys.−

Trypsin

−Asn.Met. Phe. Cys. Ala .Gly. Tyr .Leu.Glu. Gly . Lys .Asn.−

Ser . Cys.Gln. Gly. Gly.Asp.SER.Gly. Pro.   −   Val .Cys.−

HISTIDINE LOOP

Chymotrypsin-A

−Thr. Gly. Phe.HIS. Phe. Cys. Gly. Gly. Ser .Leu.   −   Ile .Asn.−

Glu.Asn. Try. Val . Val .Thr. Ala . Ala .HIS.Cys . Gly. Val . Thr.−

Trypsin

− Ser . Gly. Tyr .HIS. Phe. Cys. Gly. Gly. Ser .Leu.   −   Ile .Asn.−

Ser .Gln.Try.   −   Val . Ser . Ala . Ala .HIS.Cys. Tyr. Lys. Ser .

FIGURE 7. Active centre sequences in trypsin and chymotrypsin. Similarities are underlined, and the "active" histidine and serine residues are in capitals. Trypsin sequences from Walsh *et al.* (1964) and Smillie and Hartley (1964).

8(a)). In the deacylation step (Figure 8(b)), attack of this water molecule on the acyl carbonyl bond initiates the catalytic hydrolysis. One comment about this mechanism is that in detail it is almost certainly wrong, since it is written in only two dimensions. My previous remarks have suggested that I believe the crucial feature of the catalyses to be the steric disposition of the relevant atoms in the transition state which is induced by substrate binding, and I fear that we shall have to toss this question to the crystallographers.

REFERENCES

Abrash, H. I. and Niemann, C. (1963). *Biochemistry* **2**, 947.
Applewhite, T. H., Martin, R. B. and Niemann, C. (1958). *J. Amer. chem. Soc.* **80**, 1457.
Applewhite, T. H. and Niemann, C. (1959). *J. Amer. chem. Soc.* **81**, 2208.
Brown, J. R. and Hartley, B. S. (1963). *Biochem. J.* **89**, 59P.
Brown, J. R. and Hartley, B. S. (1964). Fed. European Biochem. Soc., Abstract A-29.
Chervenka, C. H. and Wilcox, P. E. (1956). *J. biol. Chem.* **222**, 635.
Cunningham, L. W. and Brown, C. S. (1956). *J. biol. Chem.* **221**, 287.
Desnuelle, P. and Rovery, M. (1961). *Advanc. Protein Chem.* **16**, 139.
Erlanger, B. F. and Cohen, W. (1963). *J. Amer. chem. Soc.* **85**, 348.
Foster, R. J. (1961). *J. biol. Chem.* **236**, 2461.

Glazer, A. N. and Sanger, F. (1963). *Biochem. J.* **90**, 92.

Gray, W. R. and Hartley, B. S. (1963). *Biochem. J.* **89**, 379.

Gutfreund, H. and Hammond, B. R. (1959). *Biochem. J.* **73**, 526.

Hartley, B. S. (1960). *Ann. Rev. Biochem.* **29**, 45.

Hartley, B. S. (1962). *Brookhaven Symp. Biol.* **15**, 85.

Hartley, B. S. (1963). "Proc. 5th Internat. Congr. Biochem., Moscow, 1961", Vol. 4 p. 104. Pergamon Press, Oxford.

Hartley, B. S. (1964). *Nature, Lond.* **201**, 1284.

Jones, J. B. and Niemann, C. (1962). *Biochemistry* **1**, 1093.

Jones, J. B. and Niemann, C. (1963). *Biochemistry* **2**, 498.

Keil, B., Prusík, Z. and Šorm, F. (1963). *Biochim. biophys. Acta* **78**, 559.

Koshland, D. E., Strumeyer, D. H. and Ray, W. J. (1962). *Brookhaven Symp. Biol.* **15**, 101.

Martin, C. J., Golubow, J. and Axelrod, A. E. (1959). *J. biol. Chem.* **234**, 295.

Massey, V. and Hartley, B. S. (1956). *Biochim. biophys. Acta* **21**, 361.

Meedom, B. (1958). *Biochim. biophys. Acta* **30**, 429.

Neurath, H. (1964). *Fed. Proc.* **23**, 1.

Neurath, H. and Hartley, B. S. (1959). *J. cell. comp. Physiol.* **54**, 179.

Schoellman, G. and Shaw, E. (1963). *Biochemistry* **2**, 252.

Smillie, L. B. and Hartley, B. S. (1964). Fed. European Biochem. Soc., Abstract A-30.

Vaslow, F. and Doherty, D. G. (1953). *J. Amer. chem. Soc.* **75**, 928.

Walsh, K. A., Kauffman, D. L., Kumar, K. S. V. S. and Neurath, H. (1964). *Proc. nat. Acad. Sci., Wash.* **51**, 301.

Wolf, J. D. and Niemann, C. (1963). *Biochemistry* **2**, 493.

Similarities in the Sequence of Trypsin and Chymotrypsin

T. Hofmann

Department of Biochemistry, University of Washington, Seattle, U.S.A.

As Dr. Keil and Dr. Hartley have pointed out, the amino acid sequences around two of the three histidines, and around the "active centre" serine of trypsinogen, are almost identical with those in chymotrypsinogen. Cyanogen bromide cleavage (Hofmann, 1964) have shown that all three histidines of trypsinogen are located in the N-terminal region while the "active centre" serine is in the C-terminal region of the peptide chain and thus, like the corresponding residues in chymotrypsinogen, are widely separated along the peptide chain. Walsh *et al.* (1964) have given the exact positions (Figure 1). When compared with chymotrypsinogen, a close similarity becomes apparent which is even more striking when the first activation products (π-chymotrypsin and trypsin) are compared. In the first step in the activation, a peptide bond is split and this gives rise to a new N-terminal tripeptide sequence which is identical in both proteins (Figure 1). On numbering the positions of the residues from this common point one finds that the "histidine loop" and the "active centre" serine are apparently within two residues of the same position in the two molecules. (The pentapeptide Ileu.Asn.Ser.Gln.Try occupies either position 66–70 or 36–40 (Walsh *et al.*, 1964). The latter position is shown here because as Dr. Hartley has pointed out, the "histidine loops" in trypsin and chymotrypsin then have virtually identical structures.)

Also, as shown by Dr. Keil, the amino acid sequences around at least three of the disulphide bridges are similar. The cyanogen bromide studies showed that most of the half-cystine residues in trypsinogen are located beyond residue 92 and indicated another similarity to chymotrypsinogen. Comparing the exact positions of the half-cystines in trypsinogen (Walsh *et al.*, 1964) with those of chymotrypsinogen confirms this similarity.

Trypsinogen   13, 31, 42 or 47, 115, 122, 143, 154, 168, 179, 189, 203, 216.
Chymotrypsinogen 1, 42, 58, 122, 136, 168, 182, 191, 201, 221.

There is a striking concentration of the half-cystine residues in the C-terminal half of the two molecules. Thus, in spite of large differences in the primary sequences, features essential for activity and overall structures of the two molecules are identical.

REFERENCES

Hofmann, T. (1964). *Biochemistry* 3, 356.
Walsh, K. A., Kauffman, D. L., Kumar, K. S. V. S. and Neurath, H. (1964). *Proc. nat. Acad. Sci., Wash.* **51**, 301.

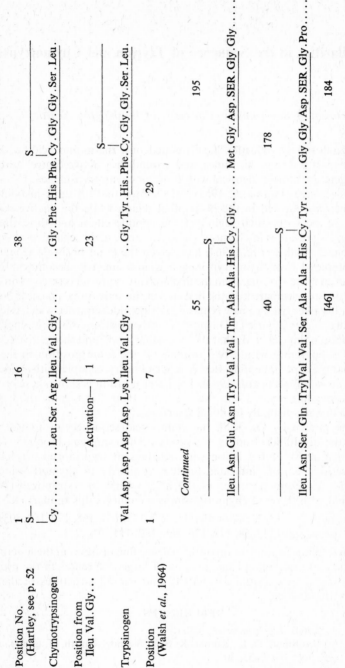

FIGURE 1. Comparison of positions of residues in trypsinogen and chymotrypsinogen. Sequences underlined are identical.

The Tryptic "Core" of the C-Chain of α-Chymotrypsin

S. Maroux, M. Rovery and P. Desnuelle

Institut de Chimie Biologique, Faculté des Sciences, Marseille, France

The primary structure of bovine chymotrypsinogen A has been studied for the last five years. In the course of these studies, several structures were suggested. As pointed out by Hartley (1962), many unusual difficulties were encountered, one of them arising from the fact that bovine chymotrypsinogen A contains more than 200 residues in a single peptide chain. Many peptides are formed by the various enzymes used for the degradation of the protein and it is sometimes difficult to locate them properly.

A technique able to eliminate this kind of difficulty is to separate the three open chains of α-chymotrypsin, the N-terminal A-chain containing only 13 residues and already investigated by Meedom (1958), the B-chain located in the centre of the molecule and the C-terminal C-chain. Unfortunately, the preparation of B- and C-chains in a pure form turned out to be rather tricky. We managed some years ago (Dinh van Hoang, Rovery and Desnuelle, 1962) to purify the performic acid oxidized C-chain by chromatography on Sephadex G50. The material thus obtained was about 96% pure and its analysis disclosed a series of interesting facts: (a) the C-chain contains about 100 residues instead of 50 as originally believed; (b) it is devoid of histidine, with the consequence that both histidines of chymotrypsin are located in the B-chain; (c) it is also devoid of phenylalanine, with the consequence that a phenylalanine-containing peptide formerly considered as belonging to the C-terminal region should be displaced; (d) it contains 5 half-cystine residues. Since the A-chain has one of these residues, the B-chain should contain four. All these facts were fully confirmed by subsequent and more detailed studies.

Some months later (Dinh van Hoang, Rovery and Desnuelle, 1963), the B- and C-chains were purified after reductive sulphitolysis of α-chymotrypsin, the technique used being chromatography on DEAE-cellulose in 8 M urea. The results are shown in Figure 1. In a phosphate gradient at pH 8·0, the C-chain emerges first, followed four break through volumes later by the B-chain. Cross contamination is as low as 4%. Another advantage of DEAE-cellulose is that it possesses a higher capacity than polystyrene resins.

Similar results were obtained with the S-carboxymethylated chains after reduction of α-chymotrypsin with mercaptoethanol and subsequent alkylation. Table I recalls the amino acid composition of the chains. A satisfactory agreement exists between the amino acid composition of the oxidized and reduced C-chain, on the one hand, and between the sum of the three chains

Table I. Amino Acid Composition of the B- and C-Chains of α-Chymotrypsin

Amino acid	B-Chain Non-corrected	B-Chain Corrected	B-Chain Adopted	C-Chain Non-corrected	C-Chain Corrected	C-Chain Adopted	Oxidized C-chain	Sum A+B+C	α-ChT
Ala	11·45	11·37	11	10·25	10·40	10–11	10–11	22–23	22
Arg	1·09	1·04	1	1·75	1·78	2	2	3	3
Asp	13·19	13·26	13	8·91	8·95	9	10	22–23	21
Cys	—	—	—	—	—	—	5	—	10
Glu	10·40	10·60	10–11	4·01	3·90	4	4	15–16	14
Gly	11·51	11·44	11–12	10·41	10·55	10–11	11	23–25	23
His	1·85	1·92	2	0·00	0·00	0	0	2	2
Ileu	5·92	5·98	6	3·07	3·02	3	3	10	10
Leu	9·23	9·16	9	8·08	8·18	8	8–9	19–20	19
Lys	7·92	8·00	8	6·00	6·07	6–7	7	14–15	13–14
Met	0·09	0·00	0	1·94	2·02	2	2	2	2
Phe	5·73	6·06	6	0·22	0·00	0	0	6	6–7
Pro	3·34	3·27	3	4·17	4·30	4	5	9–10	9
Ser	13·90	13·80	14	10·40	10·10	10	11	25–26	26–29
Thr	11·70	11·70	12	9·12	9·10	9	9	21	22
Try	—	3·65	4	—	4·20	4	—	8	7–8
Tyr	1·99	1·96	2	1·90	1·93	2	2	4	4
Val	13·48	12·99	13	8·07	8·03	8	8	23	22–23
Total			129–131			96–99	101–103	238–247	235–242

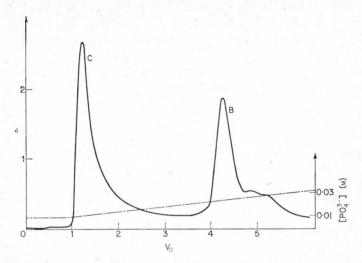

FIGURE 1. Separation of S-sulpho B- and C-chains of α-chymotrypsin on DEAE-cellulose. The column (3·2 cm × 25 cm) is equilibrated with a pH 8·0 buffer 0·01 M in phosphate and 8 M in urea. After the emergence of the first break through volume (V_0 = 200 ml), a linear gradient of phosphate (broken straight line) is started.

(A+B+C) and the known composition of α-chymotrypsin. The B-chain appears to contain about 130 residues. It was also directly confirmed that both histidine residues of the enzyme are in the B-chain, whereas the "reactive" serine is in the C-chain.

When pure B- and C-chains became available, many aspects of the primary structure of chymotrypsinogen A needed clarification. The worst situation seemed to prevail in the C-terminal region of the molecule. Thus, we decided to investigate the structure of the C-chain. Digestion of this chain with purified trypsin gives a series of soluble peptides and an insoluble "core".

Table II lists the soluble tryptic peptides arising from the S-sulpho C-chain. We did not establish the full sequence of these peptides, but merely separated them and determined their overall amino acid composition. It may be seen from Figure 2 that they agree perfectly with the sequences already worked out for this region by Hartley (1962).

As soon as the residues contained in these soluble peptides were subtracted from the total residues of the C-chain, it became apparent that the sequences suggested at that time for the C-terminal region of chymotrypsinogen were unsatisfactory. Thus, we began to study more closely the tryptic "core". Table II gives the amino acid composition of this "core". The "calculated" values are obtained by subtracting the residues of the soluble peptides from the total composition of the C-chain. The "observed" values are obtained directly by analysis. A substantial agreement exists between both sets of values, suggesting the presence of 41–42 residues in the "core".

3*

$\leftarrow$———— T_1 ————————$\rightarrow$ $\leftarrow$—————————T_2——————————$\rightarrow$
Ala.Asn.(Asx, Pro, Thr).Arg, (Ala, Asx$_2$, Cys, Glx$_2$, Leu$_4$, Pro, Ser$_2$, Thr).Lys,

$\leftarrow$————————————
$\leftarrow$————— $T_5 + T_6$ —————————
$\leftarrow T_3 \rightarrow$ $\leftarrow$——T_4————$\rightarrow$ $\leftarrow$ $T_5 \rightarrow$ $\leftarrow$—————T_6—————————
Lys, (Gly, Thr, Try, Tyr).Lys, (Ileu.Lys), (Ala$_3$, Asx$_2$, Cys$_3$, Gly$_5$, Ileu, Leu,

———·— $T_6 + T_7$ ————·—— $\rightarrow$
————————————— $\rightarrow$
——————— —— $\longrightarrow$ $\leftarrow T_7 \rightarrow$
Met$_2$, Pro, Ser$_{3,4}$, Val$_2$).Lys, Lys....

$\leftarrow T_8 \rightarrow$
Ala.Arg

FIGURE 2. Soluble tryptic peptides from the C-chain.

However, a rather interesting fact, which is discussed below in more detail, is that the "core" contains one tenth of a residue of arginine to which one tenth of a residue of alanine may easily be associated. The dipeptide Ala-Arg has already been found among the soluble peptides (Figure 2); some argu-

TABLE II. Amino Acid Composition of the Tryptic Core

Name of the residue	Number of residues			
	Calculated (C-chain soluble peptides)	Found by direct analysis	Found in peptides	Difference
Ala	4	4	4	0
Asp + Asn	3	3	3	0
1/2 Cys	1	1	1	0
Glu + Gln	2	2	2	0
Gly	4–5	5	4	0 (− 1)
Ileu	1	1	1	0
Leu	3	3	3	0
Lys	1	<1†	1	—
Pro	1	2	1	0 (− 1)
Ser	5	5	5	0
Thr	6	5	5	0
Try	3	3	2	− 1
Tyr	1	1	1	0
Val	6	5–6	6	0 (+ 1)
Ala	0	0·1†	0·1†	0
Arg	0	0·1†	0·1†	0
Total	41–42	41–42	39 + 1 (+ 2) = 42	

† See text.

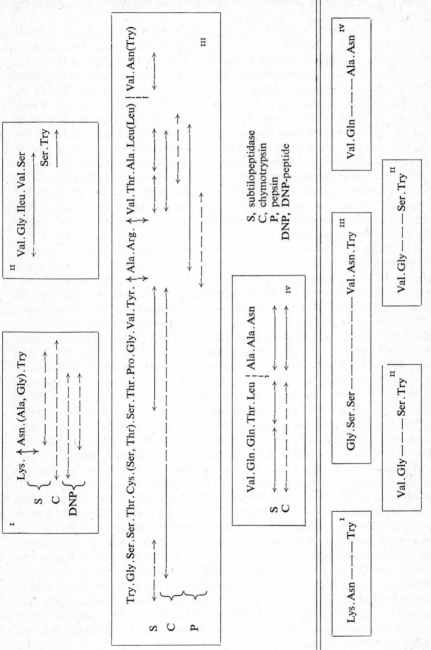

FIGURE 3. Peptides from the tryptic core of the C-chain.

ments are given below favouring the view that the sequence Ala-Arg actually belongs to the "core".

When the tryptic "core" is treated with FDNB and hydrolysed, three N-terminal residues (lysine, aspartic acid and valine) are rather unexpectedly found. The assumption formerly made by Hartley (1962) of an Ala.Arg. Val . . . sequence at the amino end of the "core" provides an easy explanation for the occurrence of large amounts of the dipeptide Ala.Arg in the soluble peptides. According to this assumption, the "core" would be a mixture of 10% intact chains and 90% of shorter chains with an N-terminal valine. Then, one is bound to suppose that the single lysine residue of the "core" occupies an internal position and that a splitting, at least partial, has also occurred at this point giving rise to the N-terminal lysine. However, the identification among the peptic peptides of a tripeptide containing the single tyrosine residue of the "core", alanine and arginine, confirms the structure worked out by Keil (1963), according to which the sequence Ala-Arg occupies an internal position and that, consequently, the "core" begins by the sequence Lys.Asn . . . .

Figure 3 gives a summary of our findings concerning the primary structure of the tryptic "core". As shown, four sequences containing all the residues of the "core" have been fairly well established by our own experiments, with two notable exceptions for which information from other sources must be used. (a) The last tryptophan residue of part III has never been found either in peptides or as the free amino acid. No actual overlap† exists at the end of this part between leucine and valine. The sequence Val.Asn.(Try) is put there in accordance with the structures already proposed by Hartley (1962) and Keil (1963). (b) Also no overlap† exists in part IV between leucine and alanine. But the C-terminal Ala.Ala.Asn sequence is very likely to be associated with the Val.Gln.Gln.Thr.Leu sequence. Leucine, threonine and valine have been repeatedly found among the amino acids liberated by carboxypeptidase from chymotrypsinogen A. Furthermore, glutamine has been qualitatively identified in the C-terminal sequence by Kassel and Laskowski (1962) and we have confirmed its presence by a quantitative method.

The final step is to put together the four parts in the right order. Part I is certainly N-terminal (see above). Part IV is C-terminal and the big part III is central. Hence, two possibilities should be considered for part II, which may be put either between I and III or between III and IV. The identification of large amounts of tryptophan in the C-terminal sequence of chymotrypsinogen is consistent with both possibilities. A little serine has been found in the C-terminal sequence by Pechère et al. (1958) but not by Kassel and Laskowski (1962). So far, we have failed to characterize serine among the free amino acids of the carboxypeptidase digests, but a final choice should be postponed until an additional overlap has been found in this region. The position assigned to the second leucine residue of part III is not certain. A peptide containing one alanine and two leucines has been found once in a subtilopeptidase digest.

† Lacking overlaps are indicated in Figure 3 by vertical dotted lines.

Apparently, during its general attack on the S-sulpho C-chain, trypsin partly splits a Lys-Asn and an Arg-Val bond.† Furthermore, a chymotrypsin-like splitting occurs between tyrosine and alanine.† Thus, free lysine and the dipeptide Ala.Arg appear in the soluble peptides fraction and most of the "core" is likely to contain two chains tightly bound together for some unknown reasons.

REFERENCES

Dinh van Hoang, Rovery, M. and Desnuelle, P. (1962). *Arch. Biochem. Biophys.* Suppl. 1, 232.

Dinh van Hoang, Rovery, M. and Desnuelle, P. (1963). *Biochim. biophys. Acta* **69**, 188.

Hartley, B. S. (1962). *Brookhaven Symp. Biol.* **15**, 85.

Kassel, B. and Laskowski, M. (1962). *J. biol. Chem.* **237**, 413.

Keil, B., Prusík, Z. and Šorm, F. (1963). *Biochim. biophys. Acta* **78**, 559.

Meedom, B. (1958). *Biochim. biophys. Acta* **30**, 429.

Pechère, J. F., Dixon, G. H., Maybury, R. H. and Neurath, H. (1958). *J. biol. Chem.* **233**, 1364.

† The bonds partly split in the "core" are indicated in Figure 3 by vertical arrows.

Characterization of a Residue Controlling the Activity and Conformation of Chymotrypsin

B. Labouesse†, K. Carlsson, Hannah L. Oppenheimer and G. P. Hess

Department of Biochemistry, Cornell University, Ithaca, New York, U.S.A.

Substrate-induced conformational changes have been shown to occur during reactions catalysed by chymotrypsin. The evidence was provided in part by measurements of difference spectra between enzyme and enzyme-substrate complexes (Wootton and Hess, 1962). This difference spectrum is characteristic of the interaction between chymotrypsin and all the substrates that have so far been examined; it is not observed when chymotrypsinogen or denatured chymotrypsin interact with substrates (Wootton and Hess, 1962; Moon, 1964). Equilibrium experiments with enzyme-substrate complexes indicate that the optical rotatory dispersion parameters, and the thermodynamic parameters of reversible, temperature-induced phase transitions depend on the nature of the substrate and differ from those of the free enzyme (Havsteen and Hess, 1962a; Labouesse *et al.*, 1962; Havsteen *et al.*, 1963).

Other experimental results suggest that the substrate-induced conformational changes could perturb the ionization behaviour of an amino group in chymotrypsin. The evidence is as follows. Kinetic studies had already demonstrated that in the stoichiometric reaction of chymotrypsin with di-isopropylphosphorofluoridate (DFP), about one mole of H^+ is released per mole of chymotrypsin in the pH region 5 to 7, as expected; however, the liberation of H^+ was found to decrease progressively above pH 7, although the formation of di-isopropylphosphoryl-chymotrypsin (DIP-chymotrypsin) still goes to completion (Moon *et al.*, 1962; Moon, 1964). Potentiometric titration of chymotrypsin and DIP-chymotrypsin in the pH region 2–10 indicates that the kinetically observed decrease in the release of H^+ can be accounted for by an uptake of hydrogen ions by the enzyme during the reaction (Moon *et al.*, 1962; Havsteen and Hess, 1964). Spectrophotometric titrations demonstrate that the tyrosyl groups exhibit identical ionization in chymotrypsin and in DIP-chymotrypsin (Havsteen and Hess, 1962b), indicating that these groups do not account for the change in ionization behaviour.

Kinetic studies of the reaction of DFP with chymotrypsin suggested that the conformational changes precede the phosphorylation of the enzyme; this was substantiated by equilibrium studies with the isolated enzyme-DFP absorption complex at low pH (Moon, 1964).

† Permanent address: Institut de Biochimie, Faculté des Sciences, Orsay, S. et O., France.

Additional experiments, reported here, were undertaken in an attempt to identify the nature of ionizing group in chymotrypsin which is perturbed during the formation of enzyme-substrate complexes (Labouesse *et al.*, 1964).

Three times-crystallized chymotrypsinogen (Worthington) was allowed to react at pH 6·7 with acetic anhydride. The product, acetyl-chymotrypsinogen, was fractionated by ammonium sulphate precipitations and chromatographed on a DEAE-cellulose column. Amino-nitrogen analysis carried out by the Van Slyke proceedure, and reaction with dinitrofluorobenzene (DNFB) indicated that the single N-terminal amino group as well as the ε-amino groups of all the lysines had been acetylated. Spectrophotometric titration indicated that two out of the four tyrosine residues were also acetylated, while the two other tyrosine residues were masked, as in native chymotrypsin and its zymogen. Acetyl-chymotrypsinogen was then activated with trypsin under conditions which lead to δ-chymotrypsin when chymotrypsinogen is used as starting material. After chromatography of the resulting material on a CM-Sephadex column, to remove trypsin, Van Slyke amino nitrogen analysis and reaction with DNFB indicated that the only free amino group was that of N-terminal isoleucine, and that the enzyme produced was acetyl-δ-chymotrypsin.

This product was then used in a comparative study of the three proteins acetyl-chymotrypsinogen, acetyl-δ-chymotrypsin, and DIP-acetyl-δ-chymotrypsin. Titration of preparations of these proteins indicated two, three, and two ionizing groups, respectively, in the pH region 6·5–10. These titration results, considered along with the analytical data, suggest that the two histidyl residues can reasonably account for the two ionizing groups in acetyl-chymotrypsinogen, and that the three groups in acetyl-δ-chymotrypsin may reasonably be identified as the two histidyl residues and one α-amino group. The group which is titrated in acetyl-δ-chymotrypsin and not titrated in DIP-acetyl-δ-chymotrypsin has a pK′ of 8·3; this suggests that the conformational change which accompanies the formation of the DIP-enzyme perturbs the single free amino group of the molecule.

There is also evidence that the free amino group of the molecule controls the activity of the enzyme. An investigation of the reaction of acetyl-δ-chymotrypsin with [^{14}C]acetic anhydride at pH 6·7 indicated that the amount of acetyl group introduced into the molecule is directly proportional to the fraction of enzyme activity lost (H. Hatano, unpublished observations, 1964). In another study, Van Slyke amino-nitrogen determination showed that the acetylation of the protein is accompanied by a parallel loss of amino groups suggesting that the single free amino group of the molecule is being acetylated (Labouesse *et al.*, 1964).

The ionization state of the α-amino group also appears to control the pH-dependent specific rotation $[\alpha]_\lambda$ of the enzyme. The enzymes δ-chymotrypsin and acetyl-δ-chymotrypsin exhibit a specific rotation, $[\alpha]_\lambda$, which is pH-dependent, suggesting that there is a pH-dependent change of conformation of the molecules. In the pH region 7–11, data for the change in $[\alpha]_\lambda$ for acetyl-δ-chymotrypsin can be analysed to show that the rotational change accompanies the H^+ dissociation of a single ionizing group with pK' of 8·5. The value of $[\alpha]_\lambda$ of acetyl-chymotrypsinogen is pH-independent, and identical to $[\alpha]_\lambda$ of acetyl-δ-chymotrypsin at pH 11. This is as expected if it is assumed that $[\alpha]_\lambda$ depends on the ionization state of the α-amino group, for this group is in peptide linkage in acetyl-chymotrypsinogen and completely unprotonated in acetyl-δ-chymotrypsin at high pH. On the other hand, the specific rotation of DIP-acetyl-δ-chymotrypsin is pH-independent and essentially the same at pH 10 as the specific rotation of acetyl-δ-chymotrypsin at pH 7·0. The α-amino group is in both cases in the same ionization state—that is, completely protonated.

It seems, therefore, that the activation of chymotrypsinogen to δ-chymotrypsin liberates an amino-terminal isoleucine residue whose ionization state controls both the conformation of the enzyme and its catalytic properties. If in the catalysis of real substrates this amino group is perturbed owing to a substrate-induced conformational change, in the manner observed in the reaction of chymotrypsin with DFP, the formation of the acyl-enzyme would occur after a pH-dependent process, while the decomposition of the acyl-enzyme would precede it: the formation of the acyl-enzyme would appear pH-dependent above pH 8·0, and the decomposition of the acyl-enzyme would appear pH-independent. This has, in fact, been observed in reactions catalysed by chymotrypsin (Bender *et al.*, 1963). Moreover, in this scheme, the principle of microscopic reversibility is not violated by the difference between the rates of formation and decomposition of the acyl enzyme in response to pH.

REFERENCES

Bender, M. L., Clement, G. E., Kézdy, F. and Zerner, B. (1963). *J. Amer. chem. Soc.* **85**, 358.

Havsteen, B. H. and Hess, G. P. (1962a). *J. Amer. chem. Soc.* **84**, 491.

Havsteen, B. H. and Hess, G. P. (1962b). *J. Amer. chem. Soc.* **84**, 448.

Havsteen, B. H., Labouesse, B. and Hess, G. P. (1963). *J. Amer. chem. Soc.* **85**, 796.

Havsteen, B. H. and Hess, G. P. (1964). *Biochem. Biophys. Res. Commun.* **14**, 313.

Labouesse, B., Havsteen, B. H. and Hess, G. P. (1962). *Proc. nat. Acad. Sci., Wash.* **48**, 2137.

Labouesse, B., Oppenheimer, H. and Hess, G. P. (1964). *Biochem. Biophys. Res. Commun.* **14**, 319.

Moon, A. Y. (1964). Ph.D. Thesis, Cornell University.

Moon, A. Y., Sturtevant, J. M. and Hess, G. P. (1962). *Fed. Proc.* **21**, 229.

Wootton, J. F. and Hess, G. P. (1962). *J. Amer. chem. Soc.* **84**, 440.

Chymotrypsinogen: Recent Progress in Crystal Structure Analysis

J. Kraut

University of California, La Jolla, California, U.S.A.

Now that so much is known about the amino acid sequence and disulphide bridges in chymotrypsin, the question of how the chain is folded up to make a biologically active structure becomes more tantalizing than ever. During the past seven years my co-workers and I have been studying the crystal structure of the zymogen, chymotrypsinogen, in the hope of finding the answer. For various crystallographic and experimental reasons the zymogen has distinct advantages over the enzyme itself, and one may reasonably expect it to have an overall structure not very different from the active enzyme. In any case, discovering what this difference is should be most enlightening. So it is perhaps not entirely out of place for me to present the following brief progress report here.

One of the most annoying characteristics of X-ray crystallography is its inability to give structural information piecemeal. We cannot, for example, examine just the region around the active site, or the disulphide bridges, or the C-chain. In fact we are finding that in the case of the cross-linked and largely non-helical proteins like chymotrypsinogen even the general course of the backbone chain cannot be decided upon in the absence of a complete structural description at the atomic level. At present, therefore, I cannot tell you very much about the molecule, but shall simply describe the steps we are taking to bring the day closer when I hope to be able to tell you everything about it.

In brief, the present situation is this (Kraut *et al.*, 1962, 1964). Intensity data for the native type F crystals and for six isomorphous heavy-atom derivatives have been extended to a minimum Bragg spacing of 4 Å by measuring 1121 additional reflections for each. The usual least-squares refinement has been carried out, and a mean "figure of merit" of 0·77 has been obtained for all 2383 phases (Blow and Crick, 1959). This compares well with a similar statistic for haemoglobin (Cullis *et al.*, 1961). Presumably, therefore, our experimentally determined phases are about as good as they were in the case of that protein crystal structure. A new set of Fourier maps was prepared in which it was evident that a significant but not dramatic improvement had resulted from the increased resolution. The outlines of the molecule are the same as before, but some of the individual backbone chains are more clearly delineated, and in some cases they are now seen to bear periodically spaced bulges which look like side chains. The backbone chains are wound up together in a very complicated manner and, unlike haemoglobin and myoglobin, there are no long straight rods characteristic of α-helix segments.

In spite of the improved detail, however, the picture is still quite confused. Disulphide bridges are certainly not obvious, although one or two can be made out with a little imagination. Also, it is still impossible to follow the backbone chain with any confidence. In fact, on the whole, it must be admitted that very little useful information has as yet been gained.

The problem, then, is how to improve the quality of our picture of the molecule. The most obvious tactic of simply collecting isomorphous replacement data at still higher Bragg angles may, I think, be dismissed. Various kinds of evidence show that the phase determining power of our heavy-atom derivatives has just about faded out at 4 Å. The plainest indication of this is that beyond about 4 Å the intensities of the parent and derivative reflections are practically indistinguishable on diffraction photographs. In other words, the heavy atom contribution to the derivative reflections becomes more and more negligible as the Bragg angle is increased. This is very probably due to disorder in the positions of the heavy atoms, resulting in abnormally high apparent temperature factors.

Now of course one could attack this problem by finding better heavy-atom derivatives and by improving the accuracy of data-collecting procedures to make better use of what is available, and these things we shall try to do. However, at present we are inclined to favour an approach that has been standard in crystal structure analysis for many years: Fourier refinement. The principle is simply to converge on the correct structure by successive approximations. In fact, most ordinary crystal structures are determined this way, at least in part. I submit, therefore, that we are to look upon our present confusing pictures merely as first approximations. Indeed, as crystal structure analyses in general go, they are probably very good first approximations, and so in cases like haemoglobin and myoglobin where the simple pattern of the α-helix underlies most of the structure one may make fairly accurate guesses as to the details. At any rate, this has been the guiding thought behind most of our efforts for the past year.

As a preliminary step to attempted Fourier refinement, it was considered essential to establish the absolute configuration of the molecule. The reason for this is simple. In guessing at a trial structure for any segment of polypeptide chain one is at the outset faced with a fourfold ambiguity: the chain may be running in either direction, and it may be in either the D or the L configuration. Knowing the absolute configuration at least reduces the odds against guessing right by a factor of two. It was found that the HgI_4^{2-} derivative gives easily measurable anomalous dispersion effects, and out of 78 Friedel pairs examined 69 showed differences of opposite sign from those predicted. The correct configuration must therefore be the mirror image of our earlier model.

We next proceeded to build models of polypeptide chain following as closely as possible whatever detail could be reasonably interpreted in the 4 Å Fourier maps. Naturally a great deal of imagination had to be exercised. Since commerically available space-filling atomic models are too heavy and their bonds too loose for convenient construction of long chains in complicated conformations we were obliged to make our own by casting the required atomic groupings in light-weight foam plastic. Several months were required to write down coordinates for 707 atoms in 107 residues making up five disconnected chain segments. This number of residues represents about 40% of the whole molecule.

Structure factors were then computed with these atomic coordinates and a new set of Fourier maps was prepared based upon the resulting phases. These now included all 9409 terms out to a minimum Bragg spacing of 2·5 Å. Best results were obtained by combining phases from the structure factor calculations with those obtained by isomorphous replacement.

We think we have learned several useful things from this rather time-consuming and laborious experiment. Most important, it appears that progress *can* be made in this manner, for the new Fourier maps clearly show additional segments of backbone chain which were not present in the originals. Secondly, we have learned that there is still a very long way to go before a reliable structure emerges. Indeed, we can now estimate that about one-quarter to one-third of the molecule must not be visible at all in the original 4 Å Fourier maps. It is also clear that most of the first trial structure must certainly be wrong in chemical terms even if it is approximately correct in its distribution of electron density. And finally, we have learned, or perhaps I should say confirmed, that the task we are setting out upon is beyond ordinary human patience. We have hopes, however, of being rescued by computers before long.

REFERENCES

Blow, D. M. and Crick, F. H. C. (1959). *Acta cryst.* **12**, 794.

Cullis, A. F., Muirhead, H., Perutz, M. F., Rossmann, M. G. and North, A. C. T. (1961). *Proc. roy. Soc.* **A265**, 15.

Kraut, J., High, D. F. and Sieker, L. C. (1964). *Proc. nat. Acad. Sci., Wash.* (in press).

Kraut, J., Sieker, L. C., High, D. F. and Freer, S. T. (1962). *Proc. nat. Acad. Sci., Wash.* **48**, 1417.

Structure of α-Chymotrypsin

D. M. Blow, B. A. Jeffery and M. G. Rossmann

Medical Research Council Laboratory of Molecular Biology,
Cambridge, England

The crystal form of α-chymotrypsin which we have been studying was discovered by Bernal, Fankuchen and Perutz (1938), and the repeating unit of the crystal contains two chymotrypsin molecules. To put this in another way, the symmetry of the crystal lattice defines a certain volume which is repeated indefinitely throughout the crystal: this is called the "asymmetric unit". In the α-chymotrypsin crystal this volume must contain two molecules. We may assume that these two molecules have a very similar internal structure, but they must have a different external environment. From the point of view of structure determination, this situation has the disadvantage that the volume whose structure is being determined is twice as large; but in return for doing the extra work, one receives two independent views of the molecular structure.

We have used some novel crystallographic techniques which essentially search the X-ray diffraction patterns for information about the relationship between the orientations and positions of the two molecules in the asymmetric unit. In a recent publication we demonstrated the solution for α-chymotrypsin, which is shown in Figure 1 (Blow *et al.*, 1964). The vertical rods represent crystallographic symmetry axes. The whole crystal structure can be superimposed on itself by a rotation of 180° about any of these axes, followed by a translational movement along them.

Rotation of 180° about a horizontal axis can superimpose one horizontal row of molecules on themselves, but cannot superimpose the whole structure. This rotation axis, therefore, is not a crystallographic symmetry axis, but a local axis which relates the two molecules of an asymmetric unit. The situation where two molecules are related by 180° rotation without translation is a very special one, but one which may be expected to be the typical method of dimerization. We use the phrase "proper dimer" to describe such a pair of molecules. In α-chymotrypsin crystals we find two types of proper dimer axes (between the "toes" and between the "heels" of adjacent molecules). Presumably only one of these is found in dimerized solutions of chymotrypsin.

We have analysed the X-ray diffraction patterns, to a resolution of 5·8 Å, for α-chymotrypsin and for two derivatives obtained by allowing complex ions to diffuse into the crystals. The complex ions added to the solution are $PtCl_4^{2-}$, which binds to four sites in the crystal, and HgI_4^{2-}, which binds predominantly to three sites. All these sites are shown in Figure 2 (two of the $PtCl_4^{2-}$ sites lie on top of one another), and all are within 2 Å of positions which satisfy the twofold axis.

79

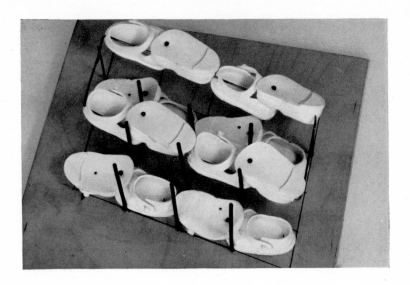

FIGURE 1. A model, constructed from asymmetric objects, illustrating the arrangement of molecules found in α-chymotrypsin. The vertical rods show the position of crystallographic twofold screw axes. (Thanks are due to Miss D. Singleton for constructing this model.)

We also have preliminary data, restricted to two dimensions, which indicate that o-chloromercuriphenol binds to a site which (in projection) lies exactly on one of the twofold axes.

By using the isomorphous replacement method, the $PtCl_4^{2-}$ and HgI_4^{2-} derivatives have been used to calculate a three-dimensional electron density map at 5·8 Å resolution. The section which passes through the level of the dimer axes shows close correspondence between electron densities at points related by the dimer axes. This provides some evidence for the accuracy of the results. A three-dimensional model, constructed by including all the density which exceeds a certain value, does not give such a good impression of the identity of the two parts of the asymmetric unit, and gives little indication of the boundary between adjacent molecules constituting a dimer. The "chains" of dimerized molecules are, however, clearly separated from each other, as previously reported (Blow et al., 1964).

In agreement with Kraut†, we find that the α-chymotrypsin molecule contains little α-helix, and it appears that the resolution will need to be considerably extended before the electron density map can be interpreted in terms of the polypeptide chain.

† J. Kraut: Chymotrypsinogen: Recent Progress in Crystal Structure Analysis. See p. 75.

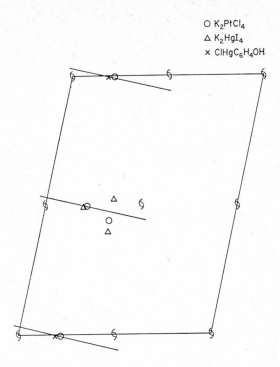

FIGURE 2. The unit cell of α-chymotrypsin, projected down the crystallographic y-axis, showing the positions of the heavy atom substituents. The symbol ϙ shows the positions of the crystallographic screw axes, and the lines show the positions of the dimer axes at the level $y = 0$. All the indicated heavy atom positions are near the level $y = 0$. The K_2PtCl_4 sites at the top and bottom of the diagram each represent two sites which lie on top of each other in projection, the dimer axis passing between them.

REFERENCES

Bernal, J. D., Fankuchen, I. and Perutz, M. F. (1938). *Nature, Lond.* **141**, 523.
Blow, D. M., Rossmann, M. G. and Jeffrey, B. A. (1964). *J. mol. Biol.* **8**, 65.

Afternoon Session

Chairman: A. Tiselius

Introduction by the Chairman

During the last ten years or so we have witnessed a tremendous development in the determination of the structure of macromolecules including biologically active proteins, e.g. enzymes. I believe that it is both significant and highly satisfactory that, at this first meeting of the Federation of European Biochemical Societies, pioneers in this field such as Fred Sanger, Max Perutz and John Kendrew are present and taking an active part. We all know that this "break through" in biochemistry came after many years of painstaking preliminaries. Today, however, one sometimes has the impression that the striking success in the field has almost caused a certain unbalance in the development of biochemical research. Information about structural details is being collected at a rate that surpasses our present possibilities of interpretation as to how these structures function. The choice of topic for today's symposium, "Structure and Activity of Enzymes", demonstrates that biochemists are aware of this problem and of the challenge it involves.

Great ingenuity is now shown in finding various approaches to this problem. Thus methods have become available to obtain preferential information about structure characteristics of the catalytic centre in an enzyme molecule, as well as about the specificity site, responsible for the attachment of the substrate. It is already clear that large parts of an enzyme molecule do not appear to be necessary for its catalytic function—at least not for *in vitro* experiments. It remains to be seen, however, if these "superfluous" parts may not have other functions, at least in the living cell to which the enzyme belongs. Thus I believe that the word "function" should involve not only the catalytic function in a narrow sense but also, for example, structural relationships responsible for the attachment of enzymes to cell structures and the interaction and coupling of enzyme systems which is so characteristic of the living cell.

May I add a personal note which appears to be relevant. When I decided to become a biochemist (some 30 years ago) after having had my training essentially in physical chemistry, my professor of organic chemistry was very worried. "Do you really believe that we will be able to understand the catalytic action of enzymes before the physical chemists have learned how catalysts work?" I remember answering that some day the physical chemists might learn that from the biochemists, which, of course, was not very polite. Nevertheless, I think that many feel today that what we now are learning about relations between structure and function of enzymes has significance beyond the purely biochemical aspects.

ACTIVE SITES

The Active Site of Esterases

R. A. OOSTERBAAN AND J. A. COHEN

Medical Biological Laboratory of the National Defense Research Organization T.N.O., Rijswijk Z.H., The Netherlands

Information on the structure and operation of the active sites of enzymes has been obtained with the aid of suitable labelling techniques. Also the study of the influence of less specific reagents on enzymic activity has led to very useful information on the identity of many essential groups in hydrolytic enzymes. Valuable information may be obtained also by the investigation of the action of hydrolytic enzymes in $H_2^{18}O$ or with [^{18}O]substrates. In this contribution some aspects of the techniques mentioned above will be discussed. Emphasis will be laid on those results which reflect our own experience in this field.

ACTIVE SERINE

It has been generally accepted that there is an analogy between the inhibition of a number of esterases and the acylating reaction which occurs during the normal substrate hydrolysis as suggested by Wilson (1960). It has been shown in many cases with [^{32}P]organo-phosphates that one molecule of inhibitor reacts with one molecule of protein with concomitant loss of enzymic activity. Chemical analyses have revealed that this reaction involves the phosphorylation of the hydroxyl group of one particular serine residue (Sanger, 1963; Cohen *et al.*, 1959). Degradation studies of the phosphorylated enzymes have revealed the amino acid sequences near this "active serine" as shown in Table I.

It is quite remarkable that the sequence dicarboxylic amino acid–serine occurs in all the enzymes of animal origin whereas the bacterial and mold proteases both contain the sequence threonine–serine. The occurrence of the dicarboxylic amino acid–serine sequence in so many esterases has led to the hypothesis (Cohen *et al.*, 1959) that this sequence is required for the activity of those enzymes. This hypothesis finds support from the kinetic evidence that a functional carboxyl group operates in acetylcholinesterase, butyrylcholinesterase (see Wilson, 1960), chymotrypsin (Bender and Clement, 1963; Stewart *et al.*, 1963), trypsin (Stewart *et al.*, 1963) and papain (Smith *et al.*, 1961). From acetyl-chymotrypsin (the intermediary acyl-enzyme formed in the course of the catalysed hydrolysis of *p*-nitrophenyl acetate) an acetyl-peptide was isolated with an amino acid sequence identical to the sequence of the corresponding phosphoryl-peptide. This stresses the analogy between the acylation step in the reaction of the enzyme with the substrate and the inhibition by organo-phosphates (Oosterbaan and van Andrichem, 1958).

TABLE I. Sequences Near the Active Serine of Some Enzymes

Sequence	Enzyme	References
Gly-Val-Ser-Ser-Cys-Met-Gly-Asp-Ser-Gly-Gly-Pro-Leu-Val-Cys-Lys NH$_2$ | Asp-Ser-Cys-Glu-Gly-Gly-Asp-Ser-Gly-Pro-Val-Cys-Ser-Gly-Lys	Chymotrypsin	Schaffer *et al.* (1957); Hartley (1961); Oosterbaan *et al.* (1958)
Asp-Ser-Gly	Trypsin	Dixon *et al.* (1958)
Asp-Ser-Gly	Thrombin	Gladner and Laki (1958)
Asp-Ser-Gly	Elastase	Naughton *et al.* (1960)
Phe-Gly-Glu-Ser-Ala-Gly(Ala, Ala, Ser)	Butyryl cholinesterase	Jansz *et al.* (1959a)
Glu-Ser-Ala	(Eel) acetylcholinesterase	Schaffer *et al.* (1954); Shaw (see Sanger, 1963)
Gly-Glu-Ser-Ala-Gly-Gly	Liver aliesterase (horse)	Jansz *et al.* (1959b)
NH$_2$ | Asp-Gly-Thr-Ser-Met-Ala-Ser-Pro-His	Subtilisin (NOVO)	Sanger and Shaw (1960); Oosterbaan *et al.* (unpublished)
Thr-Ser-Met-Ala	Mold protease (*Aspergillus oryzae*)	Shaw (see Sanger, 1963)

TABLE II. Sequences Near the Active Serine of Some Enzymes

Sequence	Enzyme	References
Thr-Ala-Ser-His-Asp	Phospho glucomutase	Milstein and Sanger (1961)
Lys-Glu-Ileu-Ser-Val-Arg (NH$_2$)	Phosphorylase	Fisher et al. (1959)
Thr-Gly-Lys-Pro-Asp-Tyr-Val-Thr-Asp-Ser-Ala-Ala-Ser-Ala	Alkaline phosphatase	Schwartz et al. (1963); Engström (1962)

TABLE III. Sequences Near the Active Cysteine of Some Enzymes

Sequence	References
Glyceraldehyde 3-phosphate dehydrogenase (yeast and muscle) Ileu-Val-Ser-Asp-Ala-Ser-Cys-Thr-Thr-Asp-Cys-Leu-Ala-Pro-Leu-Ala-Lys (NH$_2$)	Harris et al. (1963); Perham and Harris (1963); Cunningham and Schepman (1963)
Papain (tentative conclusion) Glu-Leu-Asp-Cys-Asp-Arg-Arg-Ser-Tyr	Smith et al. (1962)
Carboxypeptidase A Gly-Lys-Ala-Gly-(Ala, Ser)-Ser-(Pro, Ser, Cys)-Ser-Glu-Thr-Tyr	Vallee et al. (1960); Coombs and Omote (1962)

Additional evidence for the occurrence of an active serine in hydrolytic enzymes may be derived from the observations by Engström (1962) and Schwartz *et al.* (1963) that a serine is phosphorylated during the reaction of alkaline phosphatase with inorganic phosphate, and by Milstein and Sanger (1961) that in phosphoglucomutase an exchangeable phosphate group is bound to a serine. Moreover, the conversion of phosphorylase b into phosphorylase a in the presence of $[^{32}P]ATP$ is accompanied by introduction of a $[^{32}P]$phosphate group at a serine residue (Fisher *et al.*, 1959). The amino acid sequences around the active serine in these enzymes are depicted in Table II.

ACTIVE CYSTEINE

The action of bromo- or iodoacetic-acid on proteins has a rather broad specificity. However, the highly effective inhibitory action of these compounds in low concentrations on —SH enzymes has been attributed generally to the alkylation of the free thiol group of a cysteine residue which participates directly in the catalytic action. To this group of enzymes belongs 3-phosphoglyceraldehyde dehydrogenase which under certain conditions is able to catalyse ester hydrolysis.

The amino acid sequence around the active cysteine of this enzyme has been established by Cunningham and Schepman (1963), Harris, Meriwether and Park (1963) and Perham and Harris (1963) and the most extended amino acid sequence known is shown in Table III. During the hydrolysis of *p*-nitrophenyl acetate by this enzyme the acetyl group reacts with the same cysteine which is reactive towards iodoacetic acid. Such an observation stresses once more the importance of the SH-group in enzymic action. Papain is another SH-enzyme which is very sensitive towards inhibition by iodo- or bromoacetic acid. Once more this inhibition is caused by the alkylation of a particular cysteine. Smith *et al.* (1962) devoted much attention to the elucidation of the structure of papain. They concluded tentatively that the active cysteine residue is embedded in the peptide chain shown in Table III.

It has been stated that under certain conditions papain may be inhibited by DFP (Heinicke and Mori, 1959; Ebata *et al.*, 1962; Masuda, 1959). Masuda (1959) isolated a phosphorylated peptide containing serine, glycine, alanine and a dicarboxylic acid (or -amide). It might be interesting to investigate if there is a relation between the serine and cysteine in this enzyme.

Carboxypeptidase A needs for its activity the presence of a metal ion attached to the thiol group of a cysteine (Vallee *et al.*, 1960; Coombs and Omote, 1962). Preliminary results indicate that the sequence around this cysteine is as given in Table III.

THE ROLE OF HISTIDINE AND METHIONINE

The role of histidine in the active site of hydrolytic enzymes has been discussed by several authors (Cohen *et al.*, 1959; Barnard and Stein, 1958), Therefore we will refer here only to the experiments of Schoelmann and Shaw (1963) who found that a histidine essential for the action of chymotrypsin

$$\underset{\text{tosyl}}{\overset{\displaystyle\text{O}}{\underset{|}{\text{NH}}}}\quad\quad$$

(Structure I) Phenyl—CH$_2$CHCCH$_2$Cl with C=O above, NH below, tosyl below

(I)

(Structure II) CH$_2$CH$_2$CH$_2$CH$_2$CHCCH$_2$Cl with NH$_2$, C=O, NH, tosyl

(II)

can be alkylated with an alkylating reagent which fulfils the structural requirements of the active site. This compound (N-tosyl-L-phenylalanylchloro-
methane (I) is without effect on trypsin, but α-N-tosyl-L-lysylchloromethane
(II) fulfils the structural requirements of trypsin and is a potent inhibitor of
this enzyme; probably this inhibition equally results from the alkylation of
a histidine (Mares Guia and Shaw, 1963). The interest in the function of
methionine in the catalytic action of enzymes arose more recently. Kinetic
analyses have shown that photo-oxidation of one methionine in chymotrypsin
and phosphoglucomutase interfers with substrate hydrolysis (Ray et al.,
1960a, b; Ray and Koshland, 1963).

Schachter and Dixon (1962) have found that out of the two methionines
present in chymotrypsin the accessible residue is separated by two amino
acids from the active serine. Such a position allows an interaction between
the sulphur atom of the methionine and the hydroxyl of the active serine as
far as steric factors are concerned. At pH 3 the same methionine (the "near"
methionine) is preferentially oxidized by H_2O_2 (Koshland et al., 1962;
Schachter and Dixon, 1962; Schachter and Halliday, 1963) and alkylated by
iodoacetic acid and iodoacetamide (Schachter and Dixon, 1963). Probably
the methionine has an auxiliary function in chymotryptic action. Koshland
et al. (1962) showed that oxidation of the "near" methionine does not affect
the maximal velocity of substrate hydrolysis, but leads to a 4–5 fold increase
of K_m while Schramm and Lawson (1963) found that alkylation of one
methionine in chymotrypsin (in unknown position) with benzyl bromide
diminishes enzymic activity but does not alter the capacity to react with one
mole of DFP.

The phosphoryl-peptide isolated from subtilisin (see Table I) contained both
methionine and histidine. Recently we started an investigation to find out
whether these residues are of importance for the enzymic activity using the
photo-oxidation technique (Weil et al., 1953). We studied the photo-oxidation
of the native enzyme and of the enzyme derivative obtained after inhibition
with soman (pinacolyl methylphosphonofluoridate). In the latter case the
potential enzymic activity was estimated after the utmost reactivation of the
soman-enzyme with 0·66 M 1-methyl-2-hydroxyiminomethylpyridinium
methanesulphonate (pH 7, 30°C, 6 hr). It could be shown that both the native
enzyme and the soman-inhibited enzyme contained one "accessible" histidine
(out of 6), one "accessible" methionine (out of 5) and one "accessible"
tryptophane (out of 3). Figure 1 shows the relation between the time of exposure and the rate of disappearance of (potential) enzymic activity and the rates
of destruction of the accessible residues for the soman-inhibited enzyme.

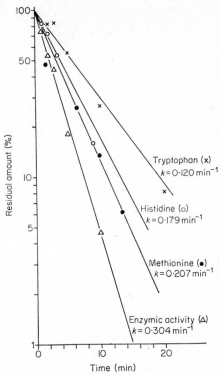

FIGURE 1. Photo-oxidation of soman-inhibited subtilisin. This diagram shows the percentages of enyzmic activity (after reactivation) and of the residual percentages of one accessible methionine, one accessible histidine and one accessible tryptophan.

We isolated from [^{32}P]soman-inhibited enzyme after photo-oxidation followed by a treatment with [^{14}C]iodoacetic acid in 7 M urea (according to the procedure described by Schachter and Dixon, 1962) a [^{32}P, ^{14}C]phosphoryl-peptide with a composition corresponding to the peptide mentioned above. Instead of methionine, however, a stoichiometric amount of the [^{14}C]carboxymethylmethionine derivative was present. Consequently it may be concluded that the "accessible" histidine and methionine of subtilisin are not located in the isolated phosphoryl-peptide (oxidized methionine does not react with iodoacetic acid). Nevertheless it does not follow from these negative findings that the methionine and the histidine of the isolated phosphoryl-peptide do not participate in the hydrolytic process of subtilisin.

RING STRUCTURES IN ESTERASES

Several authors favour the view that the unexpected reactivity of the serine in esterases is caused by the incorporation of the serine hydroxyl into covalent ring structures. Thus Rydon (1958) suggested that serine may be incorporated into an oxazoline ring. We and others (Cohen et al., 1959; Schneider, 1963; Smith et al., 1961) proposed an internal ester linkage of the serine hydroxyl with the carboxyl group of the neighbouring dicarboxylic amino acid. A fused ring, possessing a reactive hydroxyl group protruding from a double ring, has been proposed by Bernhard *et al.* (1962).

Erlanger (1960) proposed still another mechanism. According to this hypothesis the β-carboxyl group of the dicarboxylic amino acid (near the active serine) acylates the guanidyl group of an arginine residue supposed to be located in the vicinity. Thus the imino group of the acylated guanidyl group may form a hydrogen-bond with the serine hydroxyl. Recently Viswanatha (1963) discussed the possible occurrence of cycloserine in esterases.

These presumed ring structures must all be destroyed in the process which leads to the production of the peptides described previously; these were shown to consist of amino acids arrayed in a normal straight peptide chain with the substituent phosphoryl or acetyl group attached to serine.

If one assumes, as seems unavoidable, that this destructive action involves a hydrolytic mechanism, ^{18}O must be found somewhere in the acetyl-peptide when the reaction of chymotrypsin with *p*-nitrophenyl acetate as well as the breakdown of the acetylated enzyme is performed in [^{18}O]water. We carried out this experiment as follows (Oosterbaan *et al.*, 1961):

Chymotrypsin was reacted with an excess of one of its favourite substrates, *N*-acetyl-L-tyrosine ethyl ester, in [^{18}O]water at 0° and pH 6. The enzyme was then acetylated with *p*-[^{14}C]nitrophenyl acetate at pH 5 in [^{18}O]water. After elimination of excess *p*-nitrophenyl acetate the acetylated chymotrypsin was denatured in the same ^{18}O medium to stabilize the acetyl group.

Finally the acetyl chymotrypsin was digested with pancreatin, again in the presence of [^{18}O]water; this process will also result in the introduction of ^{18}O in the leucine carboxyl group in addition to the possible ^{18}O incorporation owing to hydrolytic ring breakage.

The acetyl-peptide was isolated in the usual way. It was desirable to eliminate the non-significant contribution of the leucine carboxyl group to the ^{18}O content of the acetyl-peptide. This could be achieved by splitting the hepta-peptide to give the tri-peptide, Gly.Pro.Leu and the significant tetra-peptide Gly.Asp.Acetyl-Ser.Gly. This —Gly—Gly bond was hydrolysed by incubation of the hepta-peptide with papain in water.

Table IV presents the results of the ^{18}O analysis of the two peptides. The large amount of ^{18}O in the tri-peptide corresponding to the introduction of

TABLE IV. ^{18}O Analysis of the Two Active Centre Fragments from Acetyl Chymotrypsin

Peptide	g atoms ^{18}O/mole peptide
Gly.Pro.Leu	1·57
Gly.Asp.Acetyl-Ser.Gly	0·07

For details see text.

1·57 g atoms of oxygen instead of the expected 1 g atom from the medium may be attributed to an exchange reaction between the free leucine carboxyl group formed and [^{18}O]water in the presence of pancreatin. However, the neglibible amount of ^{18}O in the tetra-peptide corresponding to the introduction of 0·07 g atom of oxygen from the medium is more pertinent to the present problem. In a number of control experiments we verified that no ^{18}O could be lost from the tetra-peptide during its preparation and isolation. The results satisfactorily prove to our mind that none of the mechanisms just listed involving covalent ring structures is likely to be involved in chymotrypsin action.

Much progress has been made in the elucidation of the primary structure around the active site of esterases. However, much more work remains to be done, since knowledge of the primary structure of esterases, though extremely important, is not in itself sufficient for the understanding of the mode of action of these enzymes. It seems to us that further progress in the immediate future will depend on our ingenuity in devising methods to analyse the physicochemical parameters which specify the active native state of proteins.

REFERENCES

Barnard, E. A. and Stein, W. D. (1958). *Advanc. Enzymol.* **20**, 51.

Bender, M. L. and Clement, G. E. (1963). *Biochem. biophys. Res. Commun.* **12**, 339.

Bernhard, S. A., Berger, A., Carter, J. H., Katchalski, E., Sela, M. and Shalitin, Y. (1962). *J. Amer. chem. Soc.* **84**, 2421.

Cohen, J. A., Oosterbaan, R. A., Jansz, H. S. and Berends, F. (1959). *J. cell. comp. Physiol.* **54**, Suppl. 1, 231.

Coombs, L. and Omote, Y. (1962). Fed. Proc. **21**, 234.

Cunningham, L. W. and Schepman, A. M. (1963). *Biochim. biophys. Acta* **73**, 406.

Dixon, G. H., Kauffmann, D. L. and Neurath, H. (1958). *J. biol. Chem.* **233**, 1373.

Ebata, M., Tsunoda, J. S. and Yasunobu, K. (1962). *Biochem. biophys. Res. Commun.* **9**, 173.

Engström, L. (1962). *Biochim. biophys. Acta* **56**, 606.

Erlanger, B. F. (1960). *Proc. nat. Acad. Sci., Wash.* **46**, 1430.

Fischer, E. H., Graves, D. J., Crittenden, E. R. S. and Krebs, E. G. (1959). *J. biol. Chem.* **234**, 1698.

Gladner, J. A. and Laki, K. (1958). *J. Amer. chem. Soc.* **80**, 1263.

Harris, I., Meriwether, B. P. and Park, J. H. (1963). *Nature, Lond.* **197**, 154.

Hartley, B. S. (1961). Proc. 5th Internat. Congress Biochem., Moscow, Symp. Iv.

Heinicke, R. M. and Mori, R. (1959). *Science* **129**, 1678.

Jansz, H. S., Brons, D. and Warringa, M. G. P. J. (1959a). *Biochim. biophys. Acta* **34**, 573.

Jansz, H. S., Posthumus, C. H. and Cohen, J. A. (1959b). *Biochim. biophys. Acta* **33**, 396.

Koshland, D. E., Strumeyer, D. H. and Ray, W. J. (1962). *Brookhaven Symp. Biol.* **15**, 101.

Mares Guia, M. and Shaw, E. (1963). *Fed. Proc.* **22**, 528.

Masuda, T. (1959). *J. Biochem., Tokyo* **46**, 1569.

Milstein, C. and Sanger, F. (1961). *Biochem. J.* **79**, 456.

Naughton, M. A., Sanger, F., Hartley, B. S. and Shaw, D. C. (1960). *Biochem. J.* **77**, 149.

Oosterbaan, R. A., Kunst, P., van Rotterdam, J. and Cohen, J. A. (1958). *Biochim. biophys. Acta* **27**, 556.

Oosterbaan, R. A. and van Adrichem, M. E. (1958). *Biochim. biophys. Acta* **27**, 423.

Oosterbaan, R. A., Jansz, H. S. and Cohen, J. A. (1961). "Proc. 5th Internat. Congress Biochem., Moscow", Abstract No. 5–28.

Perham, R. N. and Harris, J. I. (1963). *J. mol. Biol.* **7**, 316.

Ray, W. J., Ruscica, J. J. and Koshland, D. E. (1960a). *J. Amer. chem. Soc.* **82**, 4739.

Ray, W. J., Latham, H. G. and Katsoulis, M. (1960b). *J. Amer. chem. Soc.* **82**, 4743.

Ray, W. J. and Koshland, D. E. (1963). *J. Amer. chem. Soc.* **85**, 1977.

Rydon, H. N. (1958). *Nature, Lond.* **182**, 928.

Sanger, F. and Shaw, D. C. (1960). *Nature, Lond.* **187**, 872.

Sanger, F. (1963). *Proc. chem. Soc.* P76.

Schachter, H. and Dixon, G. H. (1962). *Biochem. biophys. Res. Commun.* **9**, 132.

Schachter, H. and Dixon, G. H. (1963). *Fed. Proc.* **22**, 245.

Schachter, H. and Halliday, K. A. (1963). *J. biol. Chem.* **238**, PC3134.

Schaffer, N. K., May, C. S. and Summerson, W. H. (1954). *J. biol. Chem.* **206**, 201.

Schaffer, N. K., Simet, L., Harshman, S., Engle, R. R. and Drisko, R. W. (1957). *J. biol. Chem.* **225**, 197.

Schneider, F. (1963). *Hoppe-Seyl. Z.* **332**, 38.

Schoellmann, G. and Shaw, E. (1963). *Biochemistry* **2**, 252.

Schramm, H. J. and Lawson, W. B. (1963). *Hoppe-Seyl. Z.* **332**, 97.

Schwartz, J. H., Crestfield, A. M. and Lipmann, F. (1963). *Proc. nat. Acad. Sci., Wash.* **49**, 722.

Smith, E. L., Light, A. and Kimmel, J. R. (1962). Biochemical Society Symposia No. 21. The Structure and Biosynthesis of Macromolecules, A61, p. 88. Cambridge University Press.

Stewart, J. A., Lee, H. S. and Dobson, J. E. (1963). *J. Amer. chem. Soc.* **85**, 1537.

Vallee, B. L., Coombs, T. and Hork, F. L. (1960). *J. biol. Chem.* **235**, PC45.

Viswanatha, T. (1963). *Proc. nat. Acad. Sci., Wash.* **50**, 967.

Weil, L., James, S. and Buchert, A. R. (1953). *Arch. Biochem. Biophys.* **46**, 266.

Wilson, I. B. (1960). *In* "The Enzymes", ed. by P. Boyer, H. Lardy and K. Myrbäck, 2nd Ed., Vol. 4, p. 501. Academic Press, New York.

The Structure and Catalytic Activity of Thiol Dehydrogenases

J. I. HARRIS

Medical Research Council Laboratory of Molecular Biology,
Cambridge, England

The inhibition of alcoholic fermentation in yeast and of glycolysis in muscle by iodoacetic acid was attributed to the inactivation of an "SH enzyme" (Green, Needham and Dewan, 1937; Rapkine, 1938) long before the enzyme concerned, glyceraldehyde 3-phosphate dehydrogenase (GPDH), was isolated and studied. The assumption that SH groups were involved in the inhibitor reaction has been justified in the case of GPDH but the desirability of applying chemical methods to identify the *product* formed in an enzyme-inhibitor reaction is nevertheless illustrated by the example of ribonuclease, in which inactivation by iodoacetic acid has been shown to be due to a specific reaction with histidine rather than with cysteine (Barnard and Stein, 1959; Crestfield, Stein and Moore, 1963).

Among glycolytic enzymes there is considerable evidence for the participation of SH groups in reactions catalysed by glyceraldehyde 3-phosphate, and alcohol dehydrogenases (for reviews, see Velick and Furfine, 1963; Sund and Theorell, 1963), and the selective inhibition of the pure enzymes by iodoacetic acid has led to the use of $[1-^{14}C]$iodoacetic acid for the specific labelling of "active sites" in the enzyme proteins (Harris, Meriwether and Park, 1963; Li and Vallee, 1963). This approach has also led to the chemical identification of these active sites in glyceraldehyde 3-phosphate dehydrogenase and of the sequence of amino acid residues in their immediate environment in the primary structure of the enzyme protein (Harris, Meriwether and Park, 1963; Perham and Harris, 1963). Moreover, the isolation and chemical characterization of peptide fragments containing the radioactive label has given information concerning the number and molecular size of the polypeptide chains which are joined together in a specific way to form a molecule of active enzyme.

GLYCERALDEHYDE 3-PHOSPHATE DEHYDROGENASE (GPDH)

GPDH's have been isolated in pure crystalline form from yeast and from mammalian skeletal muscle (for references, see Velick and Furfine, 1963).

The molecular weights which have been reported for GPDH's from mammalian muscle (i.e. under the conditions employed for the measurement of sedimentation and diffusion constants, partial specific volume, etc.) range between 118,000 and 138,000. Consequently the values reported for other parameters such as moles of NAD^+ bound, the total number of SH groups and the number of "reactive" SH groups, also vary and depend upon the value taken for the molecular weight of the enzyme. A value of 120,000 has been frequently used and on this basis the enzyme is assumed to bind 3 moles of NAD^+ and to contain from 11–14 SH groups, three of which are classified as highly reactive and essential for activity. It should be emphasized that these parameters apply only to molecules of *active enzyme*, and as enzyme preparations are known to lose specific activity upon repeated recrystallization and storage the actual values obtained should be related to moles of *active enzyme* rather than to moles of *enzyme protein*. If, in addition, one were to assume a value of 140,000 for the molecular weight, then the same experimentally determined results could be used to support a binding capacity for 4 moles of NAD^+ and a total content of 14–17 free SH groups, of which four are highly reactive and essential for enzyme activity.

For reasons which will be discussed later, a value of 140,000 has been adopted for the molecular weight of GPDH; the results of the experiments which are to be described have been calculated on this basis and are expressed in terms of moles of enzyme protein which may not in all cases accurately correspond to moles of *active* enzyme.

Reactions catalysed by GPDH, such as the conversion of aldehyde substrates to acyl phosphates in the presence of NAD^+ and phosphate ions, the transfer of the acyl group of acyl phosphates to acceptor molecules such as coenzyme A, and the hydrolysis of *p*-nitrophenyl acetate in the absence of NAD^+, have been shown to involve the formation of intermediate acyl-enzyme compounds. For example, an acetyl-enzyme containing 3·5–4·0 acetyl groups is formed as a stable intermediate in the enzyme catalysed hydrolysis of *p*-nitrophenylacetate (Park, Meriwether, Clodfelder and Cunningham, 1961; Taylor, Meriwether and Park, 1963). The formation of the acetyl-enzyme is inhibited by substrates of the dehydrogenase reaction as well as by co-factors, such as NAD^+ and phosphate; thus the esterase and dehydrogenase activities are mutually exclusive and both are inhibited by iodoacetic acid, which suggests that the reactions are mediated by the same reactive groups in the "active centre" of the enzyme.

REACTION WITH [1-¹⁴C]IODOACETIC ACID

GPDH from rabbit muscle was allowed to react with 8–12 equivalents of [1-^{14}C]iodoacetic acid at pH 7·0 and 0° for 4 hr. Incorporation of ^{14}C into the enzyme was measured in relation to enzyme activity; when 3·0–3·5 g atoms of ^{14}C had been incorporated per mole (140,000 g) the enzyme was found to possess less than 5% of its original activity.

The product of the enzyme-inhibitor reaction was "denatured" with acetone–HCl and digested with trypsin; when the resulting peptide mixture was submitted to ionophoresis on paper the ^{14}C was found to be associated with only one peptide (peptide TS1, Figure 1). The radioactive peptide was purified and its amino acid composition and sequence was determined as described by Harris, Meriwether and Park (1963). In a similar manner, the

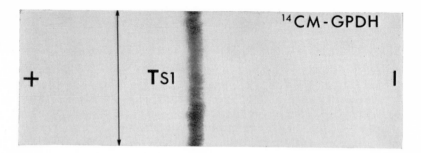

FIGURE 1. Autoradiograph of peptides containing ^{14}C produced by trypsin hydrolysis of the [1-^{14}C]iodoacetic acid derivative of glyceraldehyde 3-phosphate dehydrogenase. Ionophoresis in pyridine–acetic acid at pH 6·5.

amino acid sequence of a pepsin peptide containing the [1-^{14}C]acetyl group, introduced into the enzyme following its reaction with p-nitrophenyl [1-^{14}C]acetate, was obtained and the results of these studies are summarized in Figure 2.

(1) Lys.Ile.Val.Ser.Asn.Ala.Ser.C$\overset{*}{Y}$S.Thr.Thr.Asn.Cys

    1 2 3 4 5 6 7 8 9 10 11 12 13 14 15 16 17 18

(2) Ile.Val.Ser.Asn.Ala.Ser.C$\overset{†}{Y}$S.Thr.Thr.Asn.Cys.Leu.Ala.Pro.Leu.Ala.Lys

* S-[1-^{14}C]Acetylcysteine. † S-[1-^{14}C]Carboxymethylcysteine.

FIGURE 2. The amino acid sequence around the reactive cysteines in glyceraldehyde 3-phosphate dehydrogenase following its reaction (1) with p-nitrophenyl[1-^{14}C]acetate, (2) with [1-^{14}C]iodoacetic acid.

The results demonstrate conclusively that the reactive sites in GPDH are the SH groups of *at least* three of its constituent cysteines. These cysteines react with the inhibitor [1-^{14}C]iodoacetic acid to form S-[1-^{14}C]carboxymethylcysteine and the replacement of the SH group by the negatively charged S-carboxymethyl side chain causes a structural change in the "active centre" which prevents substrates such as glyceraldehyde 3-phosphate and p-nitrophenylacetate from being covalently bound to the enzyme. Moreover, the fact that the reactive cysteines occur in the same sequence in the primary structure shows that the "active centres" are structurally equivalent and that each molecule of active enzyme consists of at least three, and probably four, similar if not identical polypeptide chains.

Comparative studies (Perham and Harris, 1963) carried out with enzyme isolated from yeast and pig muscle have revealed that the reactive cysteines occur exclusively in the same octadecapeptide sequence as in the rabbit muscle enzyme, which shows that a remarkable structural similarity exists between enzymes from such genetically unrelated sources as yeast and mammalian muscle.

CHARACTERIZATION OF THE PEPTIDE CHAINS IN GPDH'S

(*Harris and Perham, 1963; J. I. Harris and R.N. Perham, unpublished results*) The reaction of GPDH's with $[1-^{14}C]$iodoacetic acid in 8 M urea converts *all* their constituent cysteines into $S-[1-^{14}C]$carboxymethylcysteine. When the carboxymethylated enzymes from rabbit, pig, and yeast are digested with trypsin a total of 35–40 peptide fragments are obtained in each case. In the mammalian enzymes three of these peptides are radioactive and have been shown to contain $S-[1-^{14}C]$carboxymethylcysteine; the following peptides have for example been isolated and characterized from the *pig* enzyme.

(1) Lys.Ileu.Val.Ser.Asn.Ala.Ser.CMCys.Thr.Thr.Asn.CMCys.Leu.
Ala.Pro.Leu.Ala.Lys

(2) Val.(Val$_3$Thr$_2$Ser$_1$Pro$_2$Asp$_2$Leu$_1$).CMCys.Arg

(3) Gly.(Gly$_3$His$_2$Ala$_3$Ileu$_1$Leu$_2$Phe$_3$Val$_2$Tyr$_1$Thr$_3$Ser$_4$Glu$_2$Asp$_7$ CMCys$_1$).Lys

The mammalian enzymes each contain four *unique* cysteines and the identity of sequence around each cysteine in the pig enzyme extends the area of identity between each of its constituent chains to 68 amino acids. The carboxymethylated yeast enzyme on the other hand gives rise to only one radioactive peptide (identical with peptide (1) above) showing that the enzyme protein contains only *two* unique cysteines.

If the results of amino acid analysis are expressed in terms of four residues of CMcysteine the amino acid composition shown in Table I may be derived for the protein monomer in GPDH from rabbit muscle. This corresponds to a total of 324 amino acids and to a molecular weight of 35,200; a value which is in good agreement, (a) with the yield of N-terminal valine (1 mole valine phenylthiohydantoin/35,000–38,000 g enzyme protein), obtained by the phenylisothiocyanate method; and (b) with the number of peptides (35–40) which result from the hydrolysis of the carboxymethylated enzyme derivative (in which the number of sensitive bonds; i.e. those involving the carboxyl groups of lysine and arginine residues amounts to 37, cf. Table I) with trypsin. A value of 35,000–36,000 has consequently been adopted as a working hypothesis for the molecular weight of each of the constituent chains in the enzyme; a more precise value must await the isolation and amino acid analysis of all the unique peptide fragments which are produced by hydrolysis with trypsin. It should be noted that a higher value (46,000) for the molecular weight of the protein sub-unit has been proposed by Dévényi, Sàjgo, Horvüth and Szörenyi (1963).

An interesting feature of the amino acid sequence around the reactive cysteine in GPDH is the presence of a second residue of cysteine which in the native enzyme does not react with iodoacetic acid in the presence or absence of NAD^+. Reaction of the enzyme with four equivalents of iodosobenzoate (Olson and Park, 1964) results in its complete inactivation. This

TABLE I. Amino Acid Compositions of the Protein Monomers of Glyceraldehyde 3-Phosphate Dehydrogenase from Rabbit Muscle, and Yeast Alcohol Dehydrogenase

Amino acid	GPDH	YADH
Lys	26	24
His	11	10
Arg	10	8
Asp	37	29
Thr	21	16
Ser	17	22
Glu	19	32
Pro	12	14
Gly	31	40
Ala	33	34
Val	32	32
Met	9	6
Ile	18	19
Leu	18	25
Tyr	9	14
Phe	14	8
Try	§4	§6
Cys	†‡4	‡8
Total	326	346
Mol. wt.‖	35,000	36,000

† Estimated as [1-^{14}C]CMCys.
‡ Estimated as cysteic acid.
§ Estimated spectrophotometrically.
‖ Given to the nearest thousand.

reaction has now been shown (R. N. Perham and J. I. Harris, unpublished results) to involve the simultaneous disappearance of the two SH groups in the "active centre" peptide. In the presence of cysteine (8–16 equivalents/mole) these SH groups reappear and enzymic activity is thereby restored. Structural studies on the oxidized inactive enzyme have revealed that the disappearance of the two SH groups in the presence of *o*-iodosobenzoate is due to the formation of an *intra*-chain S–S bridge in each of the protein chains in the enzyme, and this facile and reversible oxidation–reduction phenomenon may well play an important role in controlling the level of active enzyme under physiological conditions.

The results described suggest that glyceraldehyde 3-phosphate dehydrogenases as isolated and studied by physicochemical methods may be pictured as an assembly of four identical polypeptide chains which are held together by non-covalent bonds to form the quaternary structure of the active enzyme molecule; and within this polymeric form each individual chain possesses

the specific three dimensional tertiary configuration which is essential for
the manifestation of catalytic activity.

ALCOHOL DEHYDROGENASES

Alcohol dehydrogenases have been isolated as pure crystalline proteins from
yeast and from horse liver. Some of the properties of the two enzymes are
given in Table II.

TABLE II. Properties of Yeast Alcohol (YADH) and
Horse Liver Alcohol (LADH) Dehydrogenases

Enzyme properties	YADH	LADH
Molecular weight	150,000	73,000–84,000
Bound NAD^+/NADH/mole	4	2
Bound zinc (g atoms/mole)	4	2
Total SH groups	36	24–28
Essential SH groups	4	2

For references see text and Sund and Theorell (1963).

Yeast alcohol dehydrogenase (YADH) as studied by physicochemical
methods has a molecular weight of 150,000; the active enzyme binds four
moles of NAD^+, four atoms of zinc (which are essential for maintaining the
enzyme in its active configuration (Kägi and Vallee, 1960), and contains 36
free SH groups. The horse liver enzyme (LADH) has a molecular weight of
73,000–84,000; the active enzyme contains two binding sites for NAD^+,
two atoms of zinc (which are essential for activity) and 24–28 free SH groups
per mole. Both yeast and liver enzymes are inactivated by iodoacetic acid but
in contrast to glyceraldehyde 3-phosphate dehydrogenase inactivation does
not occur in the presence of coenzyme (NADH).

REACTIONS WITH [1-^{14}C]IODOACETIC ACID

Yeast and horse liver alcohol dehydrogenases were each allowed to react with
[1-^{14}C]iodoacetic acid (16 equivalents/mole enzyme) in 0·05 M phosphate
buffer at pH 7·5 and 0–4° for 12 hr. Under these conditions both enzymes
were inactivated. The inactive yeast enzyme derivative was found to contain
3·8–4·4 g atoms of ^{14}C (cf. Whitehead and Rabin, 1964; Rabin et al., 1964),
while the corresponding derivative of the liver enzyme contained 1·8–2·2
g. atoms of ^{14}C, in agreement with the results obtained by Li and Vallee
(1963).

Mercaptoethanol was added to the reaction mixtures in order to remove
excess [1-^{14}C]iodoacetic acid, and the inactive enzyme proteins were then
allowed to react with an excess of non-radioactive iodoacetic acid in 8 M urea
for 2 hr at 25°C. Urea and excess reagent were removed by dialysis against
HCl at pH 3, and the carboxymethylated enzyme derivatives were digested with

trypsin (1 % enzyme at 20°C for 2 hr). The trypsin digests were each examined by ionophoresis on paper at pH 6·5 and in both cases the [14C] incorporated into the enzyme was found mainly in *one* "neutral" peptide fragment (Figures 3 and 4).

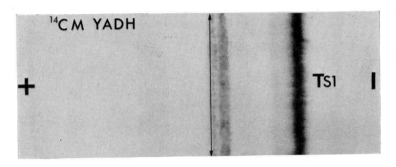

FIGURE 3. Autoradioautograph of peptides containing ^{14}C produced by trypsin hydrolysis of the [1-^{14}C]iodoacetic acid derivative of yeast alcohol dehydrogenase. Ionophoresis in pyridine–acetic acid at pH 6·5.

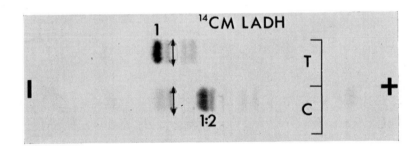

FIGURE 4. Autoradioautograph of peptides containing ^{14}C produced by trypsin hydrolysis (T) and by chymotrypsin hydrolysis (C), of the [1-^{14}C]iodoacetic acid derivative of horse liver alcohol dehydrogenase. Ionophoresis in pyridine–acetic acid at pH 6·5.

ISOLATION AND STRUCTURE OF PEPTIDES CONTAINING ^{14}C

(a) Yeast alcohol dehydrogenase

The radioactive peptide from the carboxymethylated derivative of YADH was isolated in pure form by chromatography on Sephadex G-25, followed by successive ionophoresis on paper in pyridine–acetic acid buffers at pH's of 6·5 and 6·0. The pure ^{14}C peptide was submitted to amino acid and sequence analysis and the results are given in Figure 5.

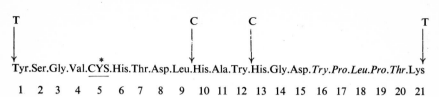

FIGURE 5. The amino acid sequence around the reactive cysteines in yeast alcohol dehydrogenase following its reaction with [1-¹⁴C]iodoacetic acid. The sequence in positions 16–20 is provisional and requires confirmation.
* S-[¹⁴C]Carboxymethylcysteine.

↓ Bonds susceptible to hydrolysis by trypsin (T) and chymotrypsin (C).

The inhibition of YADH by iodoacetic acid is shown to be due to a specific reaction with approximately four moles of cysteine per mole (150,000 g) of enzyme. The product of the reaction has been identified as S-carboxymethylcysteine, and the four reactive cysteines have been shown to occur in the same unique sequence of amino acids in the primary structure of the enzyme. This result shows that the active enzyme contains four identical reactive sites and that in all probability it consists of four similar, if not identical polypeptide chains. If the results of amino acid analysis are expressed on this basis the amino acid composition given in Table I may be derived for the protein monomer of YADH. This corresponds to a total of 346 amino acids and to a chain molecular weight of approximately 36,000. The number of peptides found in a trypsin digest of the carboxymethylated enzyme (approximately 30) agrees well with the theoretical number (32–34) based on the number of lysine and arginine residues per chain of molecular weight 36,000.

On this basis each individual chain contains one reactive SH group, and, by binding one atom of zinc and one mole of $NAD^+/NADH$, is presumably capable of forming an independent "active centre" within the quaternary structure of the active tetramer.

Kägi and Vallee (1960) showed that removal of zinc from YADH with o-phenanthroline causes irreversible inactivation which is accompanied by dissociation of the enzyme into sub-units with a molecular weight of 36,000 as determined by ultracentrifugal analysis. This led them to represent the empirical formula of the enzyme as $[(YADH)_4Zn_4] (NAD^+)_4$. The chemical results which I have described are in complete agreement with this view and show in addition that the four sub-units are chemically identical. Removal of zinc and the concomitant dissociation of the enzyme into sub-units in the presence of metal chelating agents does not occur in the presence of NADH; the coenzyme also protects the reactive cysteines against reaction with iodo-acetic acid (cf. Whitehead and Rabin, 1964). These results suggest that zinc atoms are essential for maintaining the quaternary structure of the enzyme and that both zinc and the coenzyme are bound at, or near to, each of the four reactive cysteines. The chemical nature of the other groups which are involved in the catalytic activity of the enzyme remains to be established, and in this connection the presence of two histidines in close proximity to the reactive SH groups in the primary structure could well provide additional ligand groups for binding zinc and/or NADH to the enzyme.

(b) Liver alcohol dehydrogenase

Digestion of the [1-^{14}C]iodoacetic acid derivative of LADH with trypsin gave rise to a radioactive peptide (T1) which occurred in the "neutral band" when the digest was submitted to ionophoresis on paper at pH 6·5 (Figure 4). It was consequently heavily contaminated with other neutral non-radioactive peptides and in order to facilitate the purification of the radioactive moiety the mixture of neutral peptides was submitted to further digestion with chymotrypsin. The chymotrypsin digest contained only one radioactive peptide (T1C1) which was purified by successive ionophoreses on paper at pH's of 6·5, 3·5 and 1·9. Peptide T1C1 was found to be Gly.Ile.CMCys.Arg showing that it was derived from the C-terminal part of the larger peptide T1.

Replacement of the histidine residue which occurs adjacent to the reactive cysteine in the yeast enzyme, by arginine in the liver enzyme, introduces an additional site for cleavage by trypsin. In an attempt to extend the sequence on the carboxyl side of the reactive cysteine it was decided to digest the carboxy-methylated enzyme derivative directly with chymotrypsin. When the chymo-tryptic digest was examined by ionophoresis at pH 6·5 all the ^{14}C introduced into the enzyme was found to be associated with two acidic peptide fractions; 80–85% of the ^{14}C was found in peptide C1, the remaining 15–20% being in peptide C2 (Figure 3). C1 and C2 were purified by successive ionphoreses at pH's of 6·5, 3·5 and 1·9 and were then submitted to amino acid and sequence analysis. The amino acid sequences of the radioactive peptides derived from LADH are summarized in Figure 6. The three radioactive peptides are clearly derived from the same unique sequence of amino acids.

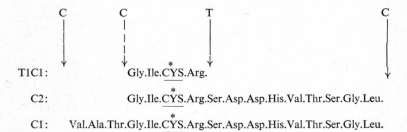

FIGURE 6. The amino acid sequences of peptides isolated from alcohol dehydrogenase from horse liver following its reaction with [1-^{14}C]iodoacetic acid.

    * S-[^{14}C]Carboxymethylcysteine.

    ↓ Bonds split by trypsin (T) and chymotrypsin (C).

The two reactive sites are identified as the SH groups of two cysteines which occur in the same sequence in the primary structure of the enzyme protein. Thus active LADH contains two structurally equivalent "active centres" and in all probability it consists of two identical polypeptide chains each with a molecular weight of 36,000–40,000. By analogy with the yeast enzyme each chain binds one mole of NAD^+, one atom of zinc and one mole of substrate; zinc is essential for activity probably because it is an essential factor in the binding of substrate and/or NAD^+ to the enzyme, and possibly too for maintaining the tertiary structure of the individual chains within the quaternary structure of the active dimer.

COMPARISON OF AMINO ACID SEQUENCES AROUND THE RE-ACTIVE CYSTEINES IN YEAST AND HORSE LIVER ALCOHOL DEHYDROGENASES

The amino acid sequences around the reactive cysteines in YADH and LADH may be compared as shown in Figure 7.

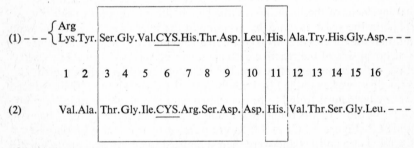

FIGURE 7. Comparison of amino acid sequences around the reactive cysteines in alcohol dehydrogenases from yeast (1) and horse liver (2).

In marked contrast to the results obtained with glyceraldehyde 3-phosphate dehydrogenases the amino acid sequence around the reactive cysteines in alcohol dehydrogenases from yeast and mammal are significantly different. Of particular interest is the replacement of the histidine residue (position 7) adjacent to the reactive cysteine in the yeast enzyme, by arginine in the mammalian enzyme, whereas the histidine in position 11 occurs in the same *relative* position in both enzymes. Mutations which have led to alterations in sequence in the immediate neighbourhood of the reactive cysteines (i.e. positions 3–9) have involved the replacement of a given amino acid by another structurally related one; thus serine, valine and threonine in the yeast enzyme have been replaced by threonine, isoleucine, and serine, respectively, in the mammalian enzyme. Outside this heptapeptide segment of the chain (i.e. positions 1–2 and 10–16, but with the exception of histidine in position 11) the sequences in the two alcohol dehydrogenases appear to be entirely unrelated (Figure 7). It may be inferred that the sequence in this part of the chain cannot be altered to any appreciable extent without at the same time affecting the tertiary structure which is essential for maintaining the structural integrity of the "active centre".

Although yeast and liver alcohol dehydrogenases catalyse the same reaction, namely the reversible oxidation and reduction of alcohols to the corresponding aldehydes (or ketones) in the presence of $NAD^+/NADH$, the enzyme proteins differ considerably in amino acid composition and molecular weight. The yeast enzyme is a tetramer with a molecular weight of 150,000 while the liver enzyme is a dimer with a molecular weight of 74,000–84,000; the former dissociates into sub-units in the presence of metal chelating agents such as o-phenanthroline while the latter enzyme does not appear to do so (Kägi and Vallee, 1960). The two enzymes also differ in their substrate and coenzyme specificities; for example, YADH reacts more rapidly with ethanol than with higher alcohols whereas LADH has a broader specificity towards carbinol compounds, and acts on long-chain primary alcohols such as Vitamin A. Thus although the "chemical" reactions catalysed by the two enzymes are the same, the actual pattern of metabolic events in liver is quite different from the process of alcoholic fermentation in yeast. The difference in biochemical environment and function of the two alcohol dehydrogenases is much more marked than is the case with the glyceraldehyde 3-phosphate dehydrogenases of yeast and mammalian muscle; and the extent of this biochemical adaptation appears to be paralleled by the correspondingly greater chemical changes which have occurred in alcohol dehydrogenases during the evolutionary development of the respective enzyme proteins. Nevertheless, in spite of the considerable differences in overall chemical composition and structure between the two alcohol dehydrogenase proteins, it is of interest to note that the fundamental structural unit in each case consists of a protein chain with a molecular weight of approximately 36,000; and that this structural unit binds one mole of $NAD^+/NADH$, one atom of zinc, and contains a reactive SH group in a sequence, which although changed, has changed in such a way as to preserve a very similar sequence of amino acids in the immediate vicinity of the reactive cysteines in the two enzymes.

DISCUSSION

The specific labelling of active sites and the study of enzyme-substrate and enzyme-inhibitor compounds by methods of structural organic chemistry has led to the identification of the chemical nature of the active sites, and to the characterization of the protein sub-units in glyceraldehyde 3-phosphate and alcohol dehydrogenases. The active forms of these enzymes are composed of an assembly of identical polypeptide chains which are held together by non-covalent bonds in such a way that each individual polypeptide chain acquires the specific three dimensional configuration which is necessary for the manifestation of catalytic activity within the quaternary "super-structure" of the active enzyme molecule.

In order to relate the structural monomer to the overall structure of the active enzyme it is necessary to obtain an accurate value for its molecular weight. It has previously been assumed (cf. Velick and Furfine, 1963) that

GPDH's from mammalian muscle contain three independent "catalytic centres" and in the light of our present knowledge this would mean that a molecule of active enzyme is a trimer with a molecular weight of 105,000–108,000. The molecular weight of the enzyme has, however, been found to be between 118,000 and 138,000 and it seems much more likely that GPDH, in common with YADH, contains *four* "catalytic centres" and that the active enzyme is a tetramer with a molecular weight of 140,000–144,000.†

The active forms of lactic dehydrogenase (LDH) have also been shown to consist of four sub-units, each with a molecular weight of approximately 35,000 (Apella and Markert, 1961; Cahn, Kaplan, Levine and Zwilling, 1962), and it is becoming increasingly apparent that a remarkable unity of structure exists between the various dehydrogenases of the glycolytic cycle. On the other hand, whereas GPDH'S and YADH appear to consist of identical polypeptide chains, active tetramers of LDH exist as a family of isoenzymes consisting, either of four identical chains, or of different proportions of two dissimilar chains.

GPDH, YADH and LDH dissociate into their respective monomeric forms under a variety of different conditions. In the case of GPDH and YADH the disruption of the quaternary structure leads to irreversible inactivation which suggests that the tertiary structure of each "active centre" is stable only within the quaternary structure of the active tetramers. With LDH's on the other hand it has been found possible to "reconstitute" active hybrid tetramers from the monomeric forms of the various isoenzymes (Markert, 1963).

When viewed in relation to some of the other proteins which have been discussed in this symposium the work which I have described on dehydrogenases is seen to be in its infancy. Nevertheless, it is now possible to envisage a structural framework for these enzymes; the bare outlines have come into focus and in terms of their chemical morphology dehydrogenases are reminiscent of haemoglobins. It is to be hoped that future studies will lead to the elucidation of the primary and tertiary structures of these dehydrogenases; only then will it become possible to give chemical reality to such ill-defined concepts as "active centres", substrate, co-enzyme and metal "binding sites" and quaternary "superstructure"; and to elucidate the precise mechanism of action of each individual enzyme, and of the inter-enzyme interactions involved in biochemical processes such as glycolysis and fermentation. One may also look forward to tracing the evolutionary development and biochemical adaptation of these enzymes in terms of their chemical structures, and to the discovery of structural relationships between enzymes which couple together to promote successive steps in a continuing cycle of biochemical reactions.

Future progress in enzymology will involve the coupled participation of the chemist, the biochemist, the enzymologist and the X-ray crystallographer,

† R. Caputto and M. Dixon (unpublished results, 1948) obtained a value of 146,000 for the molecular weight of glyceraldehyde 3-phosphate dehydrogenase from rabbit muscle (private communication from Dr. M. Dixon).

and in this respect one may be inspired and encouraged by an existing prototype, namely the successful outcome of studies which have led to the elucidation of the structure and mode of action of haemoglobins (M. F. Perutz, this symposium).

ACKNOWLEDGMENTS

The work on glyceraldehyde 3-phosphate dehydrogenases was begun at the Department of Biochemistry of the University of Cambridge, and was undertaken in collaboration with Dr. Jane Harting Park. It has since been continued in association with Mr. R. N. Perham. The experimental assistance provided by Mr. R. J. A. Turner has also been of immense value and is gratefully acknowledged.

REFERENCES

Appella, E. and Markert, C. L. (1961). *Biochem. Biophys. Res. Commun.* **6**, 171.

Barnard, E. A. and Stein, W. D. (1959). *J. mol. Biol.* **1**, 339, 350.

Cahn, R. D., Kaplan, N. O., Levine, L. and Zwilling, E. (1962). *Science* **136**, 962.

Crestfield, A. M., Stein, W. H. and Moore, S. (1963). *J. biol. Chem.* **238**, 2413.

Dévényi, T., Sàjgo, M., Horvüth, E. and Szörényi, B. (1963). *Biochim. biophys. Acta* **77**, 164.

Green, D. R., Needham, D. M. and Dewan, J. D. (1937). *Biochem. J.* **31**, 2327.

Harris, J. I., Meriwether, B. P. and Park, J. H. (1963). *Nature, Lond.* **197**, 154.

Harris, J. I. and Perham, R. N. (1963). *Biochem. J.* **89**, 60P.

Kägi, J. H. R. and Vallee, B. L. (1960). *J. biol. chem.* **235**, 3188.

Li, T-K. and Vallee, B. L. (1963). *Biochem. Biophys. Res. Commun.* **12**, 44.

Markert, C. L. (1963). *Science* **140**, 1329.

Olson, E. J. and Park, J. H. (1964). *J. biol. Chem.* (In press.)

Park, J. H. Meriwether, B. P., Clodfelder, P. and Cunningham, L. W. (1961). *J. biol. chem.* **236**, 136.

Perham, R. N. and Harris, J. I. (1963). *J. mol. Biol.* **7**, 316.

Rabin, B. R., Ruiz Cruz, J., Watts, D. C. and Whitehead, E. P. (1964). *Biochem. J.* **90**, 539.

Rapkine, L. (1938). *Biochem. J.* **32**, 1329.

Sund, H. and Theorell, H. (1963). In "The Enzymes", ed. by P. D. Boyer, H. Lardy and K. Myrbäck. Vol. 7, p. 25. Academic Press, New York.

Taylor, E. L., Meriwether, B. P. and Park, J. H. (1963). *J. biol. Chem.* **238**, 734.

Velick, S. F. and Furfine, C. (1963). In "The Enzymes", ed. by P. D. Boyer, H. Lardy and K. Myrbäck. Vol. 7, p. 243. Academic Press, New York.

Whitehead, E. P. and Rabin, B. R. (1964). *Biochem. J.* **90**, 532.

Binding of Vitamin B₆-Coenzymes and Labelling of Active Site of Enzymes by Sodium Borohydride Reduction†

EDMOND H. FISCHER

*Department of Biochemistry, University of Washington,
Seattle, Washington, U.S.A.*

The purpose of this report is to review a procedure by which the linkage and binding site of pyridoxal 5'-phosphate (PLP) to B₆-containing enzymes and the active site of certain other enzymes can be determined. The method involves the reduction of Schiff bases or imines‡ by sodium borohydride. Special attention will be paid to muscle phosphorylase since it represents the material on which the borohydride procedure was originally applied, and also because of the very unusual role PLP appears to play in this protein. Evidence for the participation of lysyl side chains in the binding of other coenzymes will also be reviewed.

BINDING OF PYRIDOXAL 5'-PHOSPHATE TO MUSCLE PHOSPHORYLASE

The borohydride procedure was devised in an attempt to clarify the function of PLP in muscle phosphorylase, and its mode of binding, as suggested by some of the spectral characteristics of the enzyme. Neutral solutions of this enzyme show, in addition to the usual protein peak at 278 mμ, a small absorption band at 330 mμ due to the presence of bound PLP (Baranowski *et al.*, 1957; Cori and Illingworth, 1957; Kent *et al.*, 1958). However, at pH values below 4·5 or above 9·5 the 330 mμ peak disappears while a new absorption maximum appears at 415 mμ (Figure 1). Simultaneously, the solution becomes intensely yellow (Kent *et al.*, 1958). These spectral changes are characteristic for the various structures displayed by PLP in combination with amines, amino acid, peptides or proteins and correspond to the formation of Schiff bases or their related forms, carbinolamines, amino acetals, substituted aldamine derivatives, etc.

On the basis of its spectral properties and in view of the stability of the PLP–enzyme complex, it was proposed (Kent *et al.*, 1958) that at neutral pH, PLP is bound to muscle phosphorylase as a substituted aldamine derivative, presumably of a free amino group of the protein, with absorption at 330 mμ (structure I, Figure 2). In acid or base solutions, or under conditions

---

† This work was supported by grants from the National Science Foundation (GB-239) and the National Institutes of Health (A-859), USPHS.

‡ For the sake of simplicity, the term Schiff base will be used to designating imines of the type RHC=N—R', irrespective of the aromatic or aliphatic nature of the substituents R and R'. Strictly speaking, it should be restricted to those imines in which R represents an aryl group.

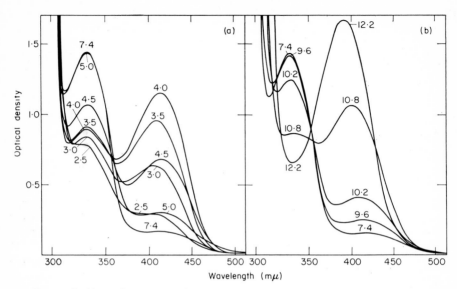

FIGURE 1. Absorption spectra of phosphorylase *b* titrated to low (a) and high (b) pH values. Concentration of protein 28 mg/ml.

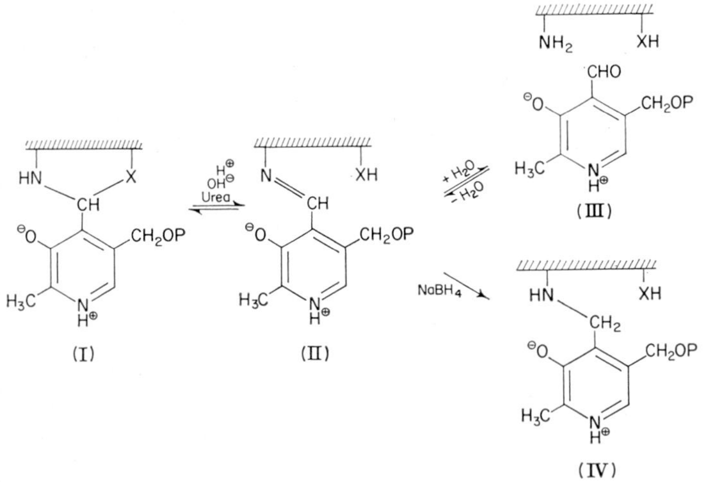

FIGURE 2. NaBH₄ reduction of muscle phosphorylase.

leading to a change in conformation of the protein, e.g. treatment with urea or detergents, form (I) is converted into the yellow Schiff base (II). The formation of the C=N azomethine bond in conjugation with the pyridine ring is responsible for the appearance of the 415 mμ absorption maximum depicted in Figure 1; this Schiff base is highly polarized and tends to hydrolyse rapidly, giving a mixture of apoenzyme and free PLP (III).

The above assumptions were confirmed by the finding that the Schiff base (II) could be quantitatively reduced to the colourless form (IV) by sodium borohydride. To this effect, a suspension of the enzyme in 50% ammonium sulphate at 0°C was brought to pH 5·0 by addition of an acetate buffer which would convert it into the Schiff base, and immediately reduced by addition of an excess of aqueous $NaBH_4$. The whole operation was carried out in a centrifuge to minimize denaturation by foaming. The reduced protein could be crystallized after dialysis (Kent, 1959) (Figure 3).

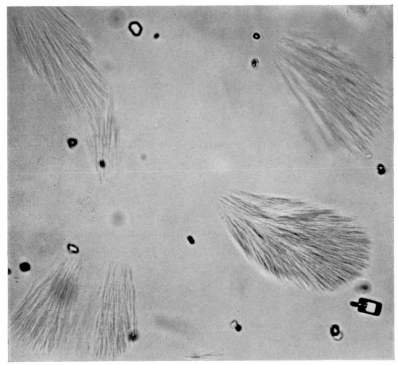

FIGURE 3. Crystalline $NaBH_4$-reduced phosphorylase b.

First, as expected, the PLP became bound to the protein in a form (secondary amine) no longer easily hydrolysed by acid or base, and therefore highly suitable for structural determination studies. Secondly, no reduction by borohydride took place at neutral pH where phosphorylase displays the spectral properties of form I. Of course, alternate structures could be postulated, such as those proposed by Christensen (1958) for certain PLP-amino acid or PLP-peptide complexes (non-hydrogen bonded Schiff bases in which the pyridoxal ring is in the zwitterionic form (V) or perhaps the carbinolamines (VI) derived from them) (Figure 4).

However, if such structures prevailed in phosphorylase, it would not be easy to explain the absence of reduction observed at neutrality. It would imply, for instance, that in phosphorylase, form (V) is not reduced because it is non-protonated; furthermore, that protonation is greatly hindered with a pK as low as 4·3. Against this assumption is the fact that glutamic aspartic transaminase and the Schiff base of phosphorylase obtained at high pH can be reduced under alkaline conditions. Lack of reactivity of form (VI) would

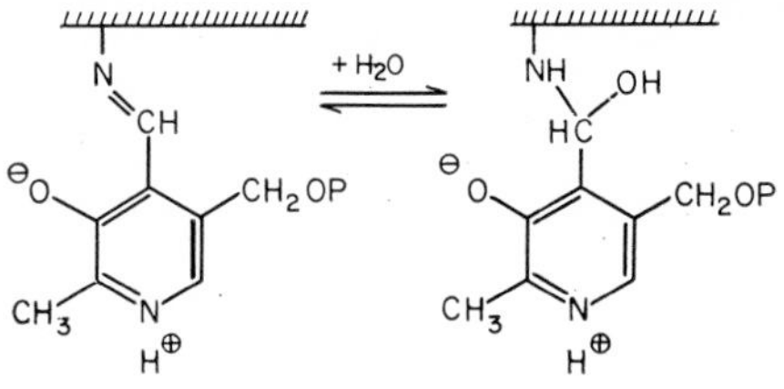

FIGURE 4. Possible alternate structures for the "330-form" of phosphorylase.

imply that hydration of the imine bond to the carbinolamine is essentially irreversible. In the structure (I) proposed above, it is assumed that a nucleophilic group of the protein (thiol, amino, imidazole, etc., denoted as X in Figure 2) attacks the imine carbon to form a stable substituted aldamine derivative. It is further assumed that the amino acid side chains furnishing the groups N and X in structure (I) are situated at some distance from one another on the peptide chain—or even on separate chains—so that distortion of the protein molecule as brought about by urea or certain detergents would cleave the aldamine structure to give the Schiff base (II) even at neutrality. However, the nature of group X has not been established.

The third and certainly most surprising observation was that NaBH$_4$-reduced phosphorylases *b* and *a* were found to retain essentially all of their catalytic activities: their behaviour during interconversion (phosphorylase *b* to *a* catalysed by phosphorylase kinase, and *a* to *b* catalysed by phosphorylase phosphatase) was perfectly normal (Krebs and Fischer, 1962). Native and reduced enzymes have essentially identical optimum pH and pH-dependence curves; their kinetic behaviour measured in the direction of glycogen synthesis or during arsenolysis of glycogen, their Michaelis constants for glucose 1-phosphate and AMP, and energies of activation are very similar. Since Illingworth *et al.* (1958) had shown that removal of PLP from phosphorylase leads to complete inactivation of the enzyme reversed by readdition of PLP, it follows (a) that no gross modifications or alterations in the structure of the protein occur during borohydride reduction; (b) that no redistribution of PLP within the molecule takes place; and (c) that in this particular instance PLP must function differently than in other PLP-containing enzymes which require its potential aldehyde group. There is no exchange of the phosphate group of PLP with inorganic phosphate, the phosphate of glucose 1-phosphate, AMP, or the phosphate introduced into the protein during the conversion of phosphorylase *b* to *a*.

No direct catalytic function of PLP has yet been found. In a study made by Dr. Jerry Hedrick, phosphorylase was incubated, with or without AMP, glycogen and α-ketoglutarate, at pH 6·8 and 8·5 with 16 different amino acids; and the reaction mixtures were analysed for possible deamination, decarboxylation, transamination or elimination reactions. None were detected. Likewise, attempts to discover a non-enzymic catalysis of glucose transfer or phosphate release in reaction mixtures containing glucose 1-phosphate, glycogen and a number of pyridoxal derivatives (pyridoxine, pyridoxal, pyridoxamine, PLP, pyridoxamine phosphate, ε-N-pyridoxyl-lysine and poly-ε-N-pyridoxylpolylysine) all failed. The reactions were carried out for 60 min at 100°C at pH 4·7, 7·0 and 9·6, with or without Al^{3+} ions. Furthermore, attempts to inactivate phosphorylase by photodecomposition of PLP with monochromatic light at various wave lengths according to Meister's procedure (Nishimara, 1962) for the preparation of β-aspartic apodecarboxylase, were totally unsuccessful. The only photoinactivation observed was in the region of 273–278 mμ where absorption is due to the aromatic amino acids. On the other hand, many observations tend to indicate that the binding of PLP to the phosphorylase molecule has profound influence on the conformation of the enzyme. Illingworth et al. (1958) have shown that PLP-free phosphorylase a (apophosphorylase a) is partially dissociated into monomer units and that apophosphorylase b shows a more heterogeneous ultracentrifuge pattern which is restored to normal upon addition of PLP. The apoenzymes are also much more subject to urea denaturation than the holoenzymes (Fischer et al., 1963).

Therefore, unless it can be shown that another functional group of PLP participates directly in the catalysis, one would have to assume that the role of the coenzyme is purely structural, maintaining the protein in the proper conformation for enzymic activity. Why a protein which could draw upon a number of ways to stabilize its tertiary or quaternary structure (e.g. amide bonds involving ε-NH_2 groups of lysine, ester bonds, metal ions, disulphide, hydrogen, electrostatic or hydrophobic bonds, etc.) should rely on this particular vitamin derivative is still a complete mystery.

BINDING OF PLP TO MUSCLE PHOSPHORYLASE b

Chymotrypsin attack of $NaBH_4$-reduced phosphorylase yielded a strongly fluorescent pyridoxylpeptide which was purified by conventional techniques. The material was ninhydrin-positive, with an absorption maximum at 325 mμ, and reacted with dichloroquinone chloroimide and diazotized p-aminoacetophenone. It was identified as the dipeptide ε-N-pyridoxyl-phosphatelysylphenylalanine.

Attempts to obtain larger fragments following tryptic attack of the reduced enzyme met with unusual difficulties; under even mild conditions (particularly during Dowex-50 chromatography or butanol–acetic acid paper chromatography) there occurred an unexplained degradation of the pyridoxyl nucleus resulting in a total loss of characteristic chemical and spectral properties. Pure ε-pyridoxyl-lysine treated under the same conditions (in the cold and in the dark to avoid photo-oxidations) appeared to be quite stable, as were its derivatives substituted in the α-amino or carboxyl group. An attempt to determine the course of the degradative process by combining apophosphorylase b with [^{32}P]PLP and carrying out the whole process on the tagged pyridoxyl fragment failed: only a minor amount of ^{32}P-labelled material with the spectral characteristics of pyridoxyl peptides could be recovered. The remainder of the radioactivity was released almost uniformly in column eluates as inorganic phosphate.

BINDING OF PLP TO GLUTAMIC ASPARTIC TRANSAMINASE AND OTHER B₆-CONTAINING ENZYMES

The results with phosphorylase clearly indicated that during NaBH₄-reduction no major alteration of the structure of the protein occurred and that PLP was fixed at its normal binding site. Therefore, the method was evidently applicable to other B₆-containing enzymes.

Glutamic-aspartic transaminase (absorption maximum at 362 mμ at neutral pH) was reduced by NaBH₄ at pH 4·8 where its solutions are yellow and absorb at 430 mμ. Reduction discharged the yellow colour, shifted the absorption maximum to 330 mμ and, of course, in this case, completely inactivated the enzyme. The reduced enzyme was denatured in urea, treated with iodoacetate to block its SH-groups and subjected to extensive (24 hr) chymotryptic attack, at which time 80% of pyridoxyl material was recovered in a trichloroacetic acid supernatant. After purification by Dowex-50 and paper chromatography, a pure peptide was isolated whose partial sequence was established as follows (Hughes et al., 1962):

Ser.Thr.Glu.(Asp, Glu, Ala, Val, Ileu, ε-pyridoxylphosphatelysyl, Lys). Gly.Ser.Asp.Phe.

A somewhat similar structure (it differs by the lack of a glycyl residue in the C-terminal peptide) was recently reported by Polianovsky and Keil (1963), following the same approach: Lys.ε-pyridoxylphosphatelysyl.Ser. Asp(or AspNH₂).Phe.

It is apparent that the sequence of the pyridoxyl peptide from glutamic-aspartic transaminase is different from that obtained from phosphorylase. Neither peptide contains a cysteinyl residue in the immediate vicinity of the pyridoxyl group. This, of course, does not eliminate the possibility that a sulphhydryl group is involved in forming the substituted aldamine structure which probably exists to some extent in most of these enzymes. If this should be the case, however, it would imply that the cysteinyl residue is either far removed on the same polypeptide chain or even located on a separate chain. That other groups are responsible, e.g. the second lysyl residue found in the transaminase peptide, represents a distinct possibility.

ε-Pyridoxyllysine has also been identified in cystathionase (homoserine deaminase) and serine transhydroxymethylase (Schirch and Mason, 1963), following NaBH₄ reduction and chemical or enzymic hydrolysis. In neither case has a pyridoxyl peptide been isolated and its structure determined.

Of course, other groups on the PLP molecule must also contribute to the binding of the coenzyme to explain, for instance, the affinity of pyridoxamine phosphate for transaminases. Electrostatic interactions or hydrogen bonds with the phenolic, pyridinium or phosphate groups, hydrophobic bonds with the methyl group in position 2 may all be involved.

It is hoped that a comparative study of the structure of PLP-peptides from various B_6-enzymes will provide some information as to their catalytic activity and enzymic specificity.

LABELLING OF ACTIVE SITES OF ENZYMES BY NaBH₄-REDUCTION OF ENZYME–SUBSTRATE COMPLEXES

Sodium borohydride reduction can also be used to tag the active site of enzymes whenever imine bonds are suspected in the formation of the enzyme-substrate complex. It has been used with great success recently by Horecker and collaborators to tag the active site of aldolase and transaldolase (Horecker et al., 1961; Grazi et al., 1962a, b; Grazi et al., 1963). The formation of "active dihydroxyacetone" in the transaldolase catalysed reaction had been postulated by Racker (1952) and confirmed by the demonstration that an exchange reaction occurred between [^{14}C]dihydroxyacetone and fructose

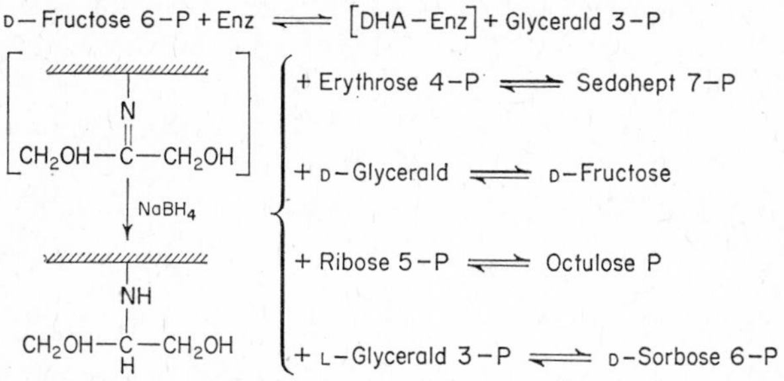

FIGURE 5. Formation of enzyme–substrate complex with transaldolase and NaBH₄ reduction (Horecker et al., 1961, 1963; Grazi et al., 1962, 1963).

6-phosphate. A stable intermediate could even be isolated by chromatography on CM-cellulose which was capable of transferring the dihydroxyacetone moiety to an acceptor aldehyde (Venkataraman and Racker, 1961). Further evidence for the existence of a stable enzyme–substrate complex was obtained by Horecker et al. (1961) by incubating transaldolase with [1-^{14}C]fructose 6-phosphate and showing that radioactivity could be transferred to erythrose 4-phosphate, glyceraldehyde, ribose 5-phosphate and other aldehydes to form the corresponding keto products, or liberated as free dihydroxyacetone by heating the enzyme at 80° (Horecker et al., 1963).

Decisive evidence for covalent binding of the substrate moiety, presumably through an imine double bond, was obtained by Horecker and collaborators by demonstrating that NaBH₄ at pH 6·0 yielded a stable 1,3-dihydroxypropyl derivative. Carbon atom 2 was implicated in the linkage since no radioactivity was released after periodate oxidation (Figure 5). Loss of enzymic activity occurred only in the presence of the substrate and to the same degree as the active site was irreversibly substituted, indicating once more that $NaBH_4$ reduction did not by itself cause denaturation of the protein (Horecker et al., 1961).

An identical approach was used in labelling the active site of aldolase in the presence of [^{14}C]- or [^{32}P]dihydroxyacetone phosphate. Upon acid hydrolysis of both aldolase and transaldolase, ε-N-(1,3-dihydroxypropyl)lysine was obtained, indicating unequivocally the direct participation of an ε-amino group of lysine in the catalysis. Uptake of one mole of dihydroxyacetone phosphate per mole of enzyme (M.W. 149,000) was observed (Grazi et al., 1962a, b). Formation of Schiff bases and their reduction by $NaBH_4$ was further observed with deoxyribose 5-phosphate aldolase and 2-keto-3-deoxy-6-phosphogluconate aldolase (Grazi et al., 1963).

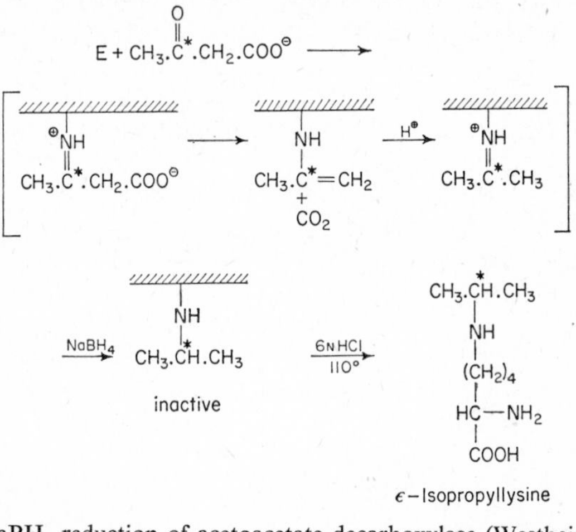

FIGURE 6. $NaBH_4$ reduction of acetoacetate decarboxylase (Westheimer, 1963).

Another example of the participation of an ε-amino group of lysine to enzymic catalysis is that of acetoacetate decarboxylase, as uncovered by the elegant word of Westheimer. Schiff base formation during the reaction had already been postulated in the mid-thirties (Pedersen, 1934; Westheimer and Cohen, 1938) and further supported by subsequent studies (e.g. Speck and Forist, 1957; Fridovitch and Westheimer, 1962). The hypothesis was essentially confirmed by Hamilton and Westheimer (1959), who showed that when acetoacetate labelled with ^{18}O in the ketonic oxygen was used as substrate, exchange of the labelled oxygen during the decarboxylation process occurred. The scheme outlined in Figure 6 was proposed for the enzymic reaction (Westheimer, 1963).

Successive $NaBH_4$ treatments of the enzyme during the reaction resulted in progressive loss of enzyme activity; here again, no loss of enzyme activity occurred in the absence of substrate. When [3-^{14}C]acetoacetate was used in the reaction, radioactivity was irreversibly introduced into the protein to the extent of 1 g atom/50,000 g protein. Upon acid hydrolysis in 6 N HCl, ε-[^{14}C]isopropyllysine was isolated (F. Westheimer, personal communication).

ROLE OF LYSYL RESIDUES IN THE BINDING OF OTHER COENZYMES

It might be appropriate at this point to mention rapidly the participation of ε-amino lysyl groups in the covalent binding of other coenzymes. Of course, in this instance, substituted amide rather than azomethine bonds are involved. The first example described is that of lipoic acid, found by Reed and co-workers to be bound to the ε-amino group of a lysyl residue in the CoA- and NAD-linked pyruvate and α-ketoglutarate dehydrogenation complexes of *Escherichia coli* (Nawa *et al.*, 1960). Recently, by partial acid hydrolysis of highly purified preparations containing bound [^{35}S]lipoic acid, Daigo and Reed (1962) determined the sequence of two lipoyl peptides, isolated from the pyruvate (I) and α-ketoglutarate (II) dehydrogenation complexes respectively:

(I) Gly.Asp.ε-lipoyllysine.Ala
(II) Thr.Asp.ε-lipoyllysine.Val.(Val, Leu).Glu

Another example is that of biotin. The isolation of biocytin (ε-N-biotinyl-L-lysine) from yeast extract (Wright *et al.*, 1952) had given a first clue as to the probable mode of binding of the coenzyme to various proteins. This assumption was confirmed in the case of propionyl carboxylase by Kosow and Lane (1962): the apoenzyme (obtained from biotin-deficient rat livers) was incubated with a cell-free liver extract which catalysed the ATP-dependent formation of propionyl holocarboxylase in the presence of d-biotin (Kosow and Lane, 1961). With [^{14}C]biotin in this system, a ^{14}C-labelled active enzyme was produced. After enzymic hydrolysis with Pronase, radioactivity was isolated in a compound identified as biocytin. No information has yet been presented as to the sequence of amino acids surrounding the biotinyl-lysyl residue.

It is clear from the above discussion that lysyl residues of certain enzymes are involved in catalysis by direct interaction with the substrate or the coenzyme. They might be therefore appropriately referred to as "lysyl enzymes" just as other enzymes have been designated as "seryl enzymes" or "sulphydryl enzymes". Reactions catalysed by several of these "lysyl" enzymes are also susceptible to straight chemical catalysis: thus, transaminations, decarboxylations, β- and γ-elimination reactions are accelerated by free PLP, just as decarboxylation of β-ketoacids is accelerated by primary amines. Of course, enzymic catalysis is much more efficient, but just how the reaction is potentiated by the presence of the protein is not known. It is not known whether certain enzymes will possess a specific amino acid sequence around the "active" lysyl residue, characteristic of a given catalytic process, or whether potentiation will primarily rely on a constellation of accessory groups brought about in the appropriate location by the tertiary conformation of the enzyme. The answer will have to await further comparative studies on the structure of lysyl-peptides obtained from enzymes of different origin or specificity, but catalysing the same reaction.

REFERENCES

Baranowski, T., Illingworth, B., Brown, D. H. and Cori, C. F. (1957). *Biochim. biophys. Acta* **25**, 16.

Christensen, H. N. (1958). *J. Amer. chem. Soc.* **80**, 99.

Cori, C. F. and Illingworth, B. (1957). *Proc. nat. Acad. Sci., Wash.* **43**, 547.

Daigo, K. and Reed, L. J. (1962). *J. Amer. chem. Soc.* **84**, 666.

Fischer, E. H., Forrey, A. W., Hedrick, J. L., Hughes, R. C., Kent, A. B. and Krebs, E. G. (1963). In "Symposium on Pyridoxal Catalysis", p. 543. Pergamon Press, Oxford.

Fridovich, I. and Westheimer, F. H. (1962). *J. Amer. chem. Soc.* **84**, 3208.

Grazi, E., Cheng, T. and Horecker, B. L. (1962a). *Biochem. Biophys. Res. Commun.* **7**, 250.

Grazi, E., Rowley, P. T., Cheng, T., Tchola, O. and Horecker, B. L. (1962b). *Biochem. Biophys. Res. Commun.* **9**, 38.

Grazi, E., Meloche, H., Martinez, G., Wood, W. A. and Horecker, B. L. (1963). *Biochem. Biophys. Res. Commun.* **10**, 4.

Hamilton, G. and Westheimer, F. H. (1959). *J. Amer. chem. Soc.* **81**, 6332.

Horecker, B. L., Pontremoli, S., Ricci, C. and Cheng, T. (1961). *Proc. nat. Acad. Sci., Wash.* **47**, 1949.

Horecker, B. L., Cheng, T. and Pontremoli, S. (1963). *J. biol. Chem.* **238**, 3428.

Hughes, R. C., Jenkins, W. T. and Fischer, E. H. (1962). *Proc. nat. Acad. Sci., Wash.* **48**, 1615.

Illingworth, B., Jansz, H. S., Brown, D. H. and Cori, C. F. (1958). *Proc. nat. Acad. Sci., Wash.* **44**, 1180.

Kent, A. B., Krebs, E. G. and Fischer, E. H. (1958). *J. biol. Chem.* **232**, 549.

Kent, A. B. (1959). Thesis, University of Washington.

Kosow, D. P. and Lane, M. D. (1961). *Biochem. Biophys. Res. Commun.* **5**, 191.

Kosow, D. P. and Lane, M. D. (1962). *Biochem. Biophys. Res. Commun.* **7**, 439.

Krebs, E. G. and Fischer, E. H. (1962). In "Advances in Enzymology", ed. by F. F. Nord, p. 263. Interscience, New York.

Nawa, H., Brady, W. T., Koike, M. and Reed, L. J. (1960). *J. Amer. chem. Soc.* **82**, 896.

Nishimara, J. S., Manning, J. M. and Meister, A. (1962). *Biochemistry* **1**, 442.

Pedersen, K. J. (1934). *J. phys. Chem.* **38**, 559.

Polianovsky, O. L. and Keil, B. (1963). *Biokhimia* **28**, 372.

Racker, E. (1954). In "Symposium on the Mechanism of Enzyme Action", ed. by W. D. McElroy and B. Glass, p. 464. The Johns Hopkins Press, Baltimore.

Schirch, L. G. and Mason, M. (1963). *J. biol. Chem.* **238**, 1032.

Speck, J. C., Jr. and Forist, A. A. (1957). *J. Amer. chem. Soc.* **79**, 4659.

Venkataraman, R. and Racker, E. (1961). *J. biol. Chem.* **236**, 1883.

Westheimer, F. H. and Cohen, H. (1938). *J. Amer. chem. Soc.* **60**, 90.

Westheimer, F. H. (1963). *Proc. chem. Soc.* 253.

Wright, L. D., Cresson, E. L., Skeggs, H. R., Wood, T. R., Peck, R. L., Wolf D. E. and Folkers, K. (1952). *J. Amer. chem. Soc.* **74**, 1996.

Studies on the Active Site of Carbonic Anhydrase

B. G. MALMSTRÖM†, P. O. NYMAN†, B. STRANDBERG AND B. TILANDER

Institute of Biochemistry and the Institute of Chemistry,
University of Uppsala, Sweden

Carbonic anhydrase is a very suitable object for studying the relationship between the structure and activity of an enzyme. The occurrence of several forms of the enzyme has been demonstrated in both bovine (Lindskog, 1960) and human erythrocytes (Nyman, 1961; Rickli and Edsall, 1962; Laurent et al., 1963), and most are available in a high degree of homogeneity. The molecular weight is relatively low, a value of about 30,000 being obtained for all forms (Lindskog, 1960; Nyman, 1961; Nyman and Lindskog, 1964). The reaction catalysed, namely the hydration of carbon dioxide, is simpler than most enzymic processes. Furthermore, the metalloprotein nature of the enzyme offers distinct advantages by providing a natural label of the "active site" (Lindskog and Malmström, 1962).

Previous studies from our laboratory have been concerned with the metal binding properties (Lindskog and Malmström, 1962; Lindskog, 1963; Lindskog and Nyman, 1964) and the amino acid composition (Nyman and Lindskog, 1964) of the various forms of the enzyme. The crystallization of one form of the human enzyme has also been described and some preliminary crystallographic data have been reported (Strandberg et al., 1962). While the stability constant for the Zn^{2+}-apoenzyme complex is very high, it has been possible to develop conditions for the reversible dissociation of the metal, which has been found necessary for activity (Lindskog and Malmström, 1962; Lindskog and Nyman, 1964). Complexes with other metal ions have also been prepared, and the highly coloured Co^{2+}-enzyme has been found to possess enzymic activity (Lindskog and Malmström, 1962). Its visible spectrum has been used to study the influence of pH and inhibitors on the immediate environment of the metal ion (Lindskog, 1963). The stability and spectral properties indicate that the metal co-ordination is the same in all forms of the enzyme (Lindskog and Nyman, 1964). As bovine carbonic anhydrase does not contain cysteine (or cystine), this would seem to exclude the idea that the single sulphydryl group of the human forms (Rickli and Edsall, 1962; Nyman and Lindskog, 1964) provides one of the ligand atoms, as suggested earlier (Rickli and Edsall, 1962).

In the present communication, we would like to describe recent developments in the crystallographic studies, which, among other things, provide clear evidence that the sulphydryl group is not involved in metal binding.

† Present address: Department of Biochemistry, University of Gothenburg, Sweden.

121

In addition we would like to discuss the recently discovered esterase activity of the enzyme, as this should provide further experimental approaches to the study of its mechanism of action.

In experiments with chemical modifications of amino acid side chains, it was found that carbonic anhydrase can split carbobenzoxy chloride catalytically. This prompted an investigation of possible esterase activity of the enzyme (cf. Tashian *et al.*, 1964). The activity of two forms of carbonic anhydrase towards different nitrophenyl esters is shown in Table I. These

TABLE I. Activity of Two Forms of Carbonic Anhydrase Towards Different Ester Substrates

	μmoles of ester per min per μmole of enzyme		
	p-Nitrophenyl acetate	*o*-Nitrophenyl acetate	Ethyl *p*-nitrophenyl carbonate
Bovine enzyme *B*	13·8	1·5	0·090
Human enzyme *B*	2·7	7·6	0·018

Conditions of measurement: 0·04 M Tris-HCl, pH 7·6; $2·87 \times 10^{-5}$ M enzyme; 4×10^{-4} M ester; 1% ethanol; 25°C.

forms of the protein differ from each other in their activity towards carbon dioxide (Nyman, 1961; Rickli and Edsall, 1962) and, as is evident from Table I, significant differences seem to occur also in their activity towards ester substrates. In similarity to the carbon dioxide reaction, the ester splitting by carbonic anhydrase is inhibited by sulphonamide inhibitors, such as Diamox (Figure 1), as well as by cyanide. The results in Figure 1 indicate that there is one esteratic site per protein molecule. The essential nature of the zinc ion for the esterase reaction is illustrated in Figure 2. The metal ion specificity of the reaction seems to be roughly the same as for the carbon dioxide reaction (Lindskog and Malmström, 1962). Thus, appreciable amounts of activity are obtained only with Zn^{2+} and Co^{2+}. Under the conditions used, the activity of the Co^{2+}-derivative of human carbonic anhydrase *B* was found to be even higher than that of the zinc-containing enzyme.

The esterase reaction of carbonic anhydrase thus seems to have many properties in common with the carbon dioxide reaction, and the findings above indicate that the same part of the enzyme functions as the active site in the esterase and hydrase reactions, possibly by mechanisms related to each other.

In further studies, special effort will be made to discern discrete steps in the esterase reaction in order to determine the precise function of the metal ion and to try to find out conditions for the isolation of intermediates, which can be used for a characterization of primary structure elements of the active centre [cf. work on chrymotrypsin (Oosterbaan *et al.*, 1962) and alkaline phosphatase (Schwartz, 1963)]. The most commonly used quasi-substrate in esterase chemistry, di-isopropylfluorophosphate (DFP), does not seem to

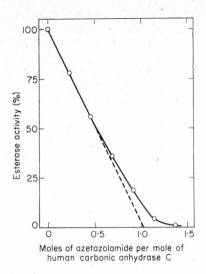

FIGURE 1. Inhibition of the esterase activity of human carbonic anhydrase C by acetazolamide (Diamox). Assay mixture: phosphate buffer, pH 7·0, $\mu = 0·08$; 4×10^{-4} M p-nitrophenyl acetate; $8·6 \times 10^{-6}$ M carbonic anhydrase C; 4% ethanol; $2–12 \times 10^{-6}$ M Diamox; 25°C.

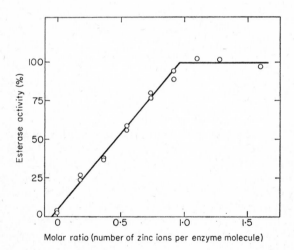

FIGURE 2. The essentiality of the zinc ion for the esterase activity of human carbonic anhydrase B. Varying amounts of a solution of Zn^{2+} ($1·5 \times 10^{-3}$ M) were added to aliquots of a solution of metal-free human carbonic anhydrase B ($1·64 \times 10^{-3}$ M) with a residual activity of 4% of the value for the native enzyme. Assay mixture: $0·08$ M phosphate buffer, pH 7·1; 1×10^{-4} M 1,10-phenanthroline; 4×10^{-4} M p-nitrophenyl acetate; 1% ethanol; $1·2–3·3 \times 10^{-5}$ M carbonic anhydrase; 25°.

interact with carbonic anhydrase. However, dimethylamidoethoxyphosphoryl cyanide (Tabun) functions as a strong inhibitor (far stronger than could be accounted for by the cyanide ion released by hydrolysis of the inhibitor). Preliminary studies with ^{32}PTabun indicate that the inhibition is connected with the binding of phosphorus to the protein molecule (Figure 3). In future work, the possibility of utilizing this approach to obtain information about the primary structure of mechanistically interesting parts of the enzyme molecule will be explored.

The results with the esterase activity of carbonic anhydrase indicate that this enzyme may in some respects be closely related to other zinc-containing esterases, such as carboxypeptidase (Vallee *et al.*, 1963) and alkaline phosphatase (Schwartz, 1963).

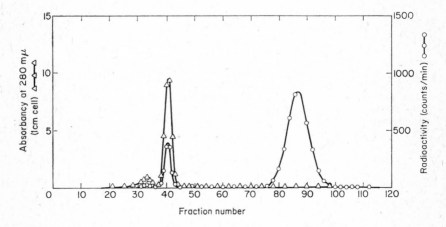

FIGURE 3. Fractionation of a mixture of ^{32}PTabun and human carbonic anhydrase *B* on a Sephadex G75 column, showing incorporation of ^{32}P into the protein.

In the X-ray crystallographic work, the zinc ion has been removed from crystalline human carbonic anhydrase *C* by soaking in a solution of 2,3-dimercaptopropanol (BAL). As the phases of the *h0l* reflections of this enzyme have been determined by means of a number of heavy atom derivatives, a few of which will be described later, it has been possible to localize the zinc atom in the *h0l* difference projection of the unit cell (Figure 4). If the zinc-free enzyme is soaked in mercury acetate solution, it takes up 1·74 equivalents of mercury as compared with 0·93 for the native protein. The mercury of the first of these derivatives is distributed on two different sites called P_1 and P_8 (Figure 5). The distance in projection between P_8 and the zinc atom is about 0·7 Å. The second mercury atom binds to the SH-group of the enzyme. This follows from Figure 6, which shows the difference electron density obtained with a derivative containing 0·91 equivalents of mercury localized to P_1. We have shown that *p*-chloromercuribenzenesulphonic acid

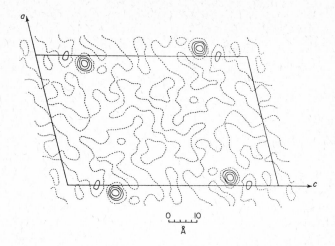

FIGURE 4. Projection along the *b*-axis of the difference in electron density between human carbonic anhydrase *C* and the zinc-free enzyme. In this, as well as in Figures 5–8, all reflections with *d* > 5·5 Å are included, and no smoothing factor has been applied.

(PCMBS) binds to the SH-group in solution. In the derivative obtained with PCMBS, P_1 is the only important site but one can also see a small peak P, which is believed to be due to the sulphonate group. As the distance $P_1 - P$ is almost the maximal one for two *p*-substitutents on a benzene ring, it is

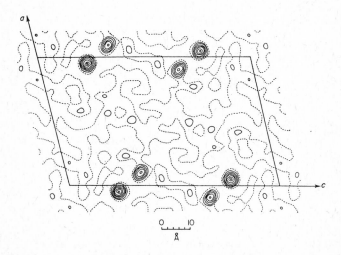

FIGURE 5. Projection along the *b*-axis of the difference in electron density between a mercury complex of zinc-free human carbonic anhydrase *C* (mercury bound to the SH-group and to a point close to the zinc position) and the zinc-free enzyme.

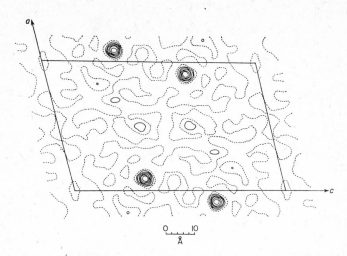

FIGURE 6. Projection along the *b*-axis of the difference in electron density between a mercurial complex of human carbonic anhydrase *C* (CH₃HgSCH₂COOH bound to the SH-group of the enzyme) and the native protein.

AcOHg-Sulphanilamide

Hg-Sulphanilamide

Hg-Salamide

Hg-Cl 13·475

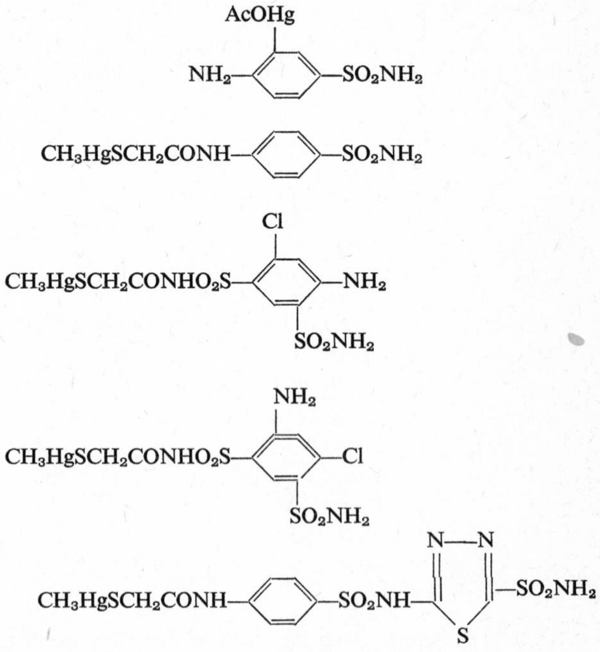

FIGURE 7. Probable formulae of mercury-containing sulphonamides used.

possible to tell almost exactly the position of the SH-group in three dimensions. The distance P_1—P_8 is about 15 Å. Thus, direct binding is excluded in the crystalline state, but the enzyme activity is still reduced to about 40% when measured under conditions where complete blocking of the SH-group with PCMBS is ensured.

Several heavy-atom derivatives have been obtained by a *specific* labelling technique (cf. Crick and Kendrew, 1958). For example, the fact that certain sulphonamides are strong and specific inhibitors of carbonic anhydrase has been utilized, and a series of mercury derivatives of sulphonamides has been synthesized (Figure 7). The difference electron density with one of these (AcOHg-Sulphanilamide) is shown in Figure 8. This derivative contains 2·1

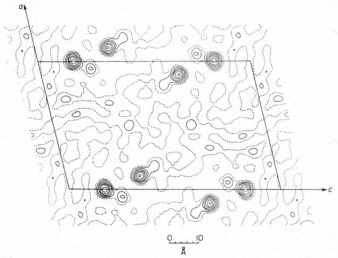

FIGURE 8. Projection along the *b*-axis of the difference in electron density between an inhibitor complex of human carbonic anhydrase *C* (AcOHg-sulphanilamide bound through mercury to the SH-group and through the sulphonic amide group of a second molecule to the active site) and the native protein.

equivalents of mercury, which are situated in the two points P_1 and P_4 (see Fig. 9). One can see small peaks P_2 and P_3, probably the sulphonamide group, close to the big ones P_1 and P_4 (compare the PCMBS-derivative). It is noted that in projection, one of the presumed sulphonamide groups (P_3) is situated close to the zinc atom.

The third co-ordinate, not visualized in the projections shown, has been determined for the points P_1, P_4, P_5, P_7 and P_8 (the projection of the unit cell with these and other sites of substituents is shown in Figure 9), some of which have already been mentioned. With the help of these data, it has been possible to get a fair appreciation of the orientation in the unit cell of a number of low molecular weight substances used in the preparation of heavy atom derivatives. From this and other evidence, some conclusions concerning the shape of the molecule may be drawn, and a three-dimensional working

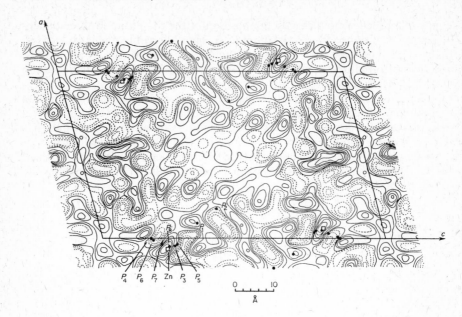

FIGURE 9. Electron density projection along the b-axis of human carbonic anhydrase C. The $F(000)$ term has been omitted in the summation; therefore, the zero contour line (the outermost dotted line) corresponds to the average electron density of the unit cell. Densities below average are indicated by dotted contours. The zinc position is especially marked. P_1, P_2 ... P_8 are the heavy atom positions.

P_1: Mercury bound to the SH-group.
P_2: Probably the position of a sulphur atom of AcOHg-sulphanilamide.
P_3: Probably the position of a sulphur atom of AcOHg-sulphanilamide.
P_4: One mercury atom of AcOHg-sulphanilamide.
P_5: One mercury atom of Hg-salamide.
P_6: Probably the position of a sulphur (and/or chlorine) atom of Hg-salamide
P_7: One mercury atom of Hg-Cl 13·475.
P_8: Position of mercury when replacing zinc.

model of the molecule has been constructed. However, this will not be discussed here, as a sufficient number of isomorphous derivatives are available so that a complete and rigorous structure determination should soon be completed.

REFERENCES

Crick, F. H. C. and Kendrew, J. C. (1958). *Advanc. Protein Chem.* **12**, 133.
Laurent, G., Castay, M., Marrig, C., Garcon, D., Charrel, M. and Derrien, Y. (1963). *Biochim. biophys. Acta* **77**, 518.
Lindskog, S. (1960). *Biochim. biophys. Acta* **39**, 218.
Lindskog, S. (1963). *J. biol. Chem.* **238**, 945.
Lindskog, S. and Malmström, B. G. (1962). *J. biol. Chem.* **237**, 1129.
Lindskog, S. and Nyman, P. O. (1964). *Biochim. biophys. Acta* **85**, 462.

Nyman, P. O. (1961). *Biochim. biophys. Acta* **52**, 1.

Nyman, P. O. and Lindskog, S. (1964). *Biochim. biophys. Acta* **85**, 141.

Oosterbaan, R. A., Adrichem, M. van and Cohen, J. A. (1962). *Biochim. biophys. Acta* **63**, 204.

Rickli, E. E. and Edsall, J. T. (1962). *J. biol. Chem.* **237**, PC 258.

Schwartz, J. H. (1963). *Proc. nat. Acad. Sci., Wash.* **49**, 871.

Strandberg, B. E., Tilander, B., Fridborg, K., Lindskog, S. and Nyman, P. O. (1962). *J. mol. Biol.* **5**, 583.

Tashian, R. E., Douglas, D. P. and Yu, Ya-Shion L. (1964). *Biochem. Biophys. Res. Commun.* **14**, 256.

Vallee, B. L., Riordan, J. F. and Coleman, J. E. (1963). *Proc. nat. Acad. Sci., Wash.* **49**, 109.

Crystallized Complexes of Liver Alcohol Dehydrogenase with Labelled Active Sites

H. THEORELL and T. YONETANI

Nobel Medical Institute, Department of Biochemistry, Stockholm, Sweden

Liver alcohol dehydrogenase (ADH) forms binary complexes with NADH or NAD$^+$, and ternary complexes with the same coenzymes and inhibitory substrate analogues. Some time ago we found that binary as well as ternary complex formation increased the stability of the enzyme molecule towards the inactivating action of (1) *p*-chloromercuribenzosulphonate, (2) heat, (3) low pH, (4) high pH. This was assumed to depend upon conformation changes in the protein molecule, caused by the complex formation in accordance with Koshland's "induced fit" theory.

In order to investigate this problem we crystallized a number of enzyme complexes: ADH–NADH; ADH–NADH–isobutyramide; ADH–NAD$^+$–pyrazole; ADH–NAD–4-iodopyrazole; and the three possible complexes of ADH, adenosine diphosphate ribose and phenanthroline. It was observed that complex formation greatly enhanced the solubility of the crystals. These crystals, and those of the free ADH are presently being studied by X-ray crystallography in collaboration with Brändén and Lindqvist at Uppsala. It should be noted that the ternary ligands isobutyramide and pyrazole occupy the active binding sites for aldehyde and alcohol respectively, and form a bridge between zinc atoms in the ADH and the co-enzymes nicotinamide moieties. These ternary complexes are therefore very stable indeed: the dissociation constants are 5×10^{-9} M for NADH from the isobutyramide complex, 10^{-8} for NAD$^+$ from the 4-iodopyrazole complex, and 10^{-7} M from the pyrazole complex.

The results hitherto obtained by X-ray crystallography verify that considerable changes occur upon complex formation. The free enzyme has orthorhombic symmetry. In the ternary complexes the symmetry is decreased to monoclin. The monoclin axis (b) is equal to the corresponding axis in free ADH ($= 181$ Å). The angle between the *a*- and *c*-axis which is 90° in free ADH is changed to about 100° in the complexes. The intensity distribution differs markedly, but certain common features can be distinguished. The unit cell in both cases contains two molecules.

We would like to emphasize the possibilities opened up by the production of crystallized complexes with iodinated pyrazoles occupying the alcohol's active site. 3,5-Di-iodo, and 3,4,5-tri-iodopyrazole also give complexes. The problem of labelling the active site with heavy atoms for studying the three-dimensional structure is therefore solved. Work on the amino acid sequence has been started in Stockholm. The optical rotatory dispersion of free enzyme and complexes is being investigated in collaboration with A. Rosenberg at Uppsala.

A Procedure which Labels the Active Centre of the Glucose Transport System of the Human Erythrocyte

W. D. STEIN

Department of Chemistry, University of Manchester, England

Glucose is transferred across the cell membrane of the human erythrocyte by a specific component of the membrane—one of the "facilitated diffusion" systems (LeFevre, 1954). This system shares many properties with enzymes— it is saturable, obeying Michaelis-Menten kinetics, is competitively inhibited by substrate analogues and is non-competitively inhibited by a variety of agents, e.g. mercury, organic mercurials and 2,4-dinitrofluorobenzene (DNFB)—which react with protein side-chains. The nature of the system, be it protein, lipid or nucleic acid, is, however, quite obscure and efforts are currently being made to isolate the system from the cell membrane so that its gross structure can be determined. Labelling the active centre of the system will, it is hoped, aid in this isolation.

The irreversible inhibition of glucose entry by dinitrofluorobenzene (Bowyer and Widdas, 1956) is the basis of this present study. DNFB inhibition is here pH-dependent, the rate of inhibition increasing fourfold as the pH is raised 1·5 units from 6·0. The rate is also markedly affected by, for instance, the presence of citrate in the reaction medium, increasing by threefold with 0·1 M citrate at pH 7·25. But most peculiar is the dependence of reaction rate on the DNFB concentration. This dependence (Figure 1) is strictly second order so that, when the DNFB concentration is increased from 1 mM to 10 mM, the rate of reaction increases some 100-fold. With the reaction conditions as pH 6·05, 0·1 M citrate, 10% ethanol and 10 mM DNFB at 25°C, the entry of sugar is 50% inhibited in 1 min of reaction time. The reaction with DNFB is stopped by a thirtyfold dilution of the reaction mixture with ice-cold saline, leading to at least a thousandfold reduction in the reaction rate. Cells separated from the dilution medium by centrifugation are washed with ice-cold saline and from these cells red cell ghosts are prepared. These ghosts have at this stage bound some 40 mµ moles of dinitrophenyl residues per ml of packed red cells, 25 mµ moles of this being in the aqueous fraction of the DNP amino acids recovered after 6 N hydrochloric acid hydrolysis of the DNP-ghosts. Most of this label is found as S-DNP cysteine (18 mµ moles/ml packed cells); 3 mµ moles is present as ε-DNP-lysine, 2 mµ moles as Im-DNP-histidine and a further 2 mµ moles is present as two unidentified components in the aqueous fraction, when these are separated by high-voltage electrophoresis at pH 3·5.

To identify the component which reacts with DNFB in a square-dependent

133

fashion, the following double-label technique was used: a red cell suspension
was divided into two portions and these were separately reacted with DNFB,
the one portion with ^{14}C-labelled DNFB at 10 mM concentration for 1 min,
the other portion with ^{3}H-labelled DNFB 1 mM for 10 min. The reactions
were stopped by cold dilution, the two preparations then *mixed* and a ghost
preparation made from the mixed, double-labelled material. The ghosts
were frozen-dried and a portion digested with papain at pH 5·3 in the presence
of cysteine for 24 hr at 37°C. The soluble peptides were separated and the
digestion terminated by precipitating an insoluble core in boiling 0·01 M
hydrochloric acid. The DNP-peptides were isolated on talc columns (a portion
of the peptides were held on the column and eluted with ethanolic trimethyl-
amine, whereas a second portion was not held on the column) and subjected

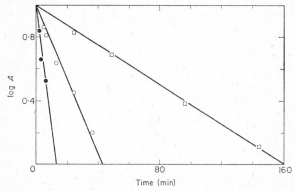

FIGURE 1. Inhibition by 2,4-dinitrofluorobenzene of sugar entry into human erythrocytes.
Ordinate: logarithm of percentage of original rate of sugar transfer remaining after various
times (min) of incubation with DNFB. Open squares: DNFB at 1 mM concentration; open
circles: at 2 mM; solid circles: at 4 mM. Rate constants (from intercepts of best straight
lines) are 152, 42 and 12 min respectively.

to high voltage ionophoresis at pH 3·5. The radioactivity in these ionophoretogram strips was assayed by counting the strips in a toluene-phosphor scintillation fluid using the Packard-TriCarb scintillation counter. A three-channel
procedure (Hendler, 1963) was used which allowed for the simultaneous assay
of the tritium and carbon counts with suitable corrections for quenching of
the phosphorescence—which was quite considerable in the yellow DNP-
peptides. From the known efficiencies of the counter for ^{14}C (23%) and for
^{3}H (2·1%) held within the chromatography paper and the known specific
activity of the ^{14}C and ^{3}H labelled DNFB used, it was possible to estimate the
yield of each DNP derivative in every peptide.

For any peptide which arises from a site reacting in a linear fashion with
DNFB, 10 min of reaction at 1 mM DNFB and 1 min of reaction at 10 mM
DNFB should yield the same amount of reaction and hence a particular
ratio of ^{3}H to ^{14}C counts in the isolated peptide. But for a peptide from a
site which reacts at a square-dependent rate with DNFB some 10 times as

much reaction should have occurred at 10 mM DNFB. Thus any "square dependent" peptide should be enriched in the ^{14}C label, i.e. have a reduced ^{3}H:^{14}C ratio. (Since the reaction with DNFB is, of course, exponential with time, the degree of enrichment with the ^{14}C label is, at 50% inhibition, in practice only sixfold and not tenfold as the simple analysis might suggest.)

In Figure 2, the ratio of ^{3}H:^{14}C counts in the major 15 peptides isolated from the papain digest (solid squares on the figure) is plotted against the number of ^{14}C counts. It can be seen that although at a low count rate the variability is rather high, the values in this experiment cluster around a ratio of 9 and no peptide present in any substantial amount has a ^{3}H:^{14}C ratio which is less than half or more than twice this amount. However, when the

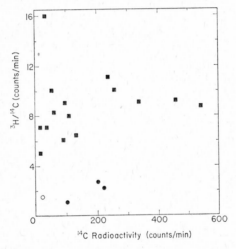

FIGURE 2. Ratio of ^{3}H: ^{14}C counts in DNP-peptides and DNP-amino acids plotted against ^{14}C counts/min in that peptide or amino acid derivative. Solid squares: DNP-peptides from soluble fraction of the papain digest; solid circles: DNP-amino acids from a 6N hydrochloric acid hydrolysate of the papain-resistant core; open circle: repurified DNP-amino acid eluted from the ionophoretogram of the papain-resistant core.

papain-resistant core was hydrolysed with 6 N hydrochloric acid and the resulting DNP amino acids separated by high voltage ionophoresis, the major peak of activity had a ^{3}H:^{14}C ratio of 2 to 2·5 (solid circles on Figure 2) and this peak following purification on talc columns and a second separation by ionophoresis yielded a spot which counted with a ^{3}H:^{14}C ratio of 1·5. A minor peak on the initial ionophoretogram counted with a ^{3}H:^{14}C ratio of 1. Figure 3 is a histogram of the ^{14}C and ^{3}H counts of this ionophoretogram. The solid line is the ^{14}C counts and the dotted line records 1/9 of the ^{3}H counts—these two curves should coincide if the material was behaving as the bulk of the peptides in the papain-solubilized fraction of the ghosts.

If the yield of ^{14}C material in this region of a number of different electrophoretograms is plotted against the degree of inhibition of sugar transfer by

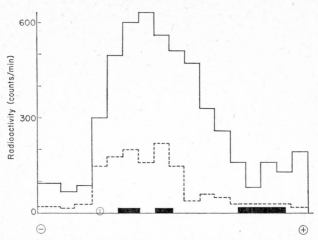

FIGURE 3. Ionophoretogram (pH 3·5, 120V/inch, 6 hr) of 6N hydrochloric acid-hydrolysate of papain-resistant core. Ordinate: counts/min in cut strip. Abscissa: distance from origin. O is the origin and the dark areas on the base line are regions containing visible DNP-amino acid. Solid line: ^{14}C counts; broken line: one-ninth of the ^{3}H counts in same strip of ionophoretogram.

DNFB in each preparation (Figure 4) a straight line is obtained. Note that two of these determinations were on material reacted at 10 mM DNFB while the remaining six were reacted at 1 mM.

Extrapolated to 100% inhibition a figure of 4·5 mμ moles of "active

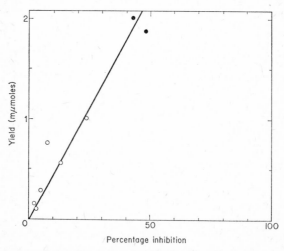

FIGURE 4. Yield of dinitrophenyl-amino acid (measured by ^{14}C assay) in mμ moles DNP isolated per ml of packed red cells. Abscissa: percentage inhibition of sugar transfer rate in corresponding sample of red cells reacted identically but with [^{12}C]dinitrofluoro-benzene.

centre" per ml of packed red cells is obtained or some 3×10^5 DNP residues at these "active centres" per red cell.

Insufficient work has been done as yet to characterize the amino acid that bears this square dependent label.

REFERENCES

Bowyer, F. and Widdas, W. F. (1956). *Disc. Faraday Soc.* **21**, 251.

Hendler, R. W. (1963). Preliminary Technical Bulletin, Nuclear-Chicago Inc.

LeFevre, P. G. (1954). *Symp. Soc. exp. Biol.* **8**, 118.

HAEMOGLOBIN

Structure and Function of Haemoglobin

M. F. PERUTZ

Medical Research Council Laboratory of Molecular Biology,
Cambridge, England

Haemoglobin has a molecular weight of 64,500. Its globin consists of four polypeptide chains and contains four haem groups, each capable of combining reversibly with molecular oxygen. However, the four iron atoms are not independent, and the equilibrium constant of any one of them is influenced by the state of oxygenation of the three others. As a result the shape of the oxygen dissociation curve is sigmoid rather than hyperbolic.

In addition to its function as an oxygen carrier, haemoglobin acts, in part indirectly, as a carrier of carbon dioxide. For each molecule of oxygen discharged, a haem-linked acid group "disappears" from haemoglobin. Its disappearance causes haemoglobin to combine either with a bicarbonate ion, to form a carbamate, or with a chloride ion, the binding of which allows a bicarbonate ion to be carried by the red cell or the serum. Conversely, the pH of the medium affects the affinity of haemoglobin for oxygen; it is greater at high than at low pH. This pH dependence is known as the Bohr effect.

Myoglobin consists of one single polypeptide chain of 153 residues and of one haem group. Its oxygen dissociation curve is hyperbolic and it shows no, or only a negligible, Bohr effect.

Physicochemical and crystallographic studies indicate that haemoglobin, but not myoglobin, undergoes a structural change in the course of its reaction with oxygen.

Detailed X-ray studies have now been made of the structure of the oxy and reduced haemoglobins of horse, and of the reduced haemoglobin of man (Cullis *et al.*, 1962; Muirhead and Perutz, 1963; Perutz, 1963; Perutz *et al.*, 1964). The results show that haemoglobin consists of four chains which are identical in pairs. Each chain has a tertiary structure closely resembling that of myoglobin; at the present limited resolution of 5·5 Å corresponding chains of human and horse haemoglobin are indistinguishably alike.

The four chains are assembled in a tetrahedral array; the haem groups are at the surface, each haem group occupying a separate pocket formed by its globin chain.

Thus the arrangement of the haems offers no clue to the mechanism of interaction between them. In the expectation that the structural change which was believed to accompany the reaction with oxygen might be more illuminating, a comparative study of the structures of reduced and oxyhaemoglobin was carried out. First results showed that reduced haemoglobin differs from the oxy form in the relative arrangement of the β-chains, which have moved apart in the reduced form, increasing the distances between their haem groups and their reactive SH-groups by 7 Å compared to those in oxyhaemoglobin. On the atomic scale this represents a striking change of structure.

We still do not know what triggers off the rearrangement, but an X-ray study of human reduced haemoglobin in which the reactive SH-groups have been blocked with N-ethylmaleimide gives a first hint. Reaction of the SH-groups with this compound reduces haem–haem interaction, while blocking with iodoacetamide does not. L. Mazzarella and Perutz found that the latter compound leaves the structure of haemoglobin unchanged, while N-ethylmaleimide produces an alteration in the structure of the β-chain immediately adjoining it, as well as alterations in the α-chain. It is hoped that a detailed X-ray study of this effect may elucidate the nature of haem–haem interaction.

REFERENCES

Cullis, A. F., Muirhead, H., Perutz, M. F., Rossman, M. G. and North, A. C. T. (1962). *Proc. roy. Soc.* **A265**, 15.

Muirhead, H. and Perutz, M. F. (1963). *Nature, Lond.* **199**, 633.

Perutz, M. F. (1963). *Science* **140**, 863.

Perutz, M. F., Bolton, W., Diamond, R., Muirhead, H. and Watson, H. C. (1964). *Nature, Lond* **203**, 687.

The Oxygen Linked Acid Groups in Haemoglobin

E. ANTONINI, J. WYMAN, M. BRUNORI, E. BUCCI,
CLARA FRONTICELLI and A. ROSSI FANELLI

*Institute of Biochemistry, University of Rome, Italy
and Regina Elena Institute for Cancer Research, Rome, Italy*

NATURE OF THE BOHR EFFECT

This communication describes recent work in this laboratory on the effect of pH on the reaction of haemoglobin with ligands, a subject which has been under investigation for more than 50 years (Bohr *et al.*, 1904; Wyman, 1948, 1964; Rossi Fanelli *et al.*, 1964).

The effect of pH on the oxygen equilibrium (the Bohr-Krogh Hasselbalch effect) is a model for pH effects in other proteins and enzymes and provides an important regulatory mechanism in respiration. Although its general features remain the same, it varies in detail from species to species. In man, the oxygen affinity ($1/p_{\frac{1}{2}}$) measured over the whole range where haemoglobin is stable (pH 5–10), is a minimum in the neighbourhood of 6·5. On the alka-

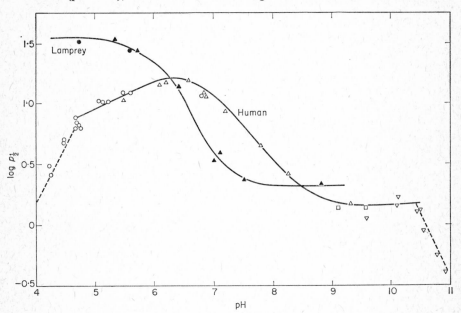

FIGURE 1. Bohr effect for human and lamprey haemoglobins (3–5 mg/ml) at 20°, 0·15–0·4 ionic strength. Human haemoglobin in ○, acetate; △, phosphate; □, borate or ▽, glycine–NaOH buffers. Larval *Lampetra planerii* haemoglobin in ●, acetate or ▲, phosphate buffers (Antonini *et al.*, 1962, 1964b).

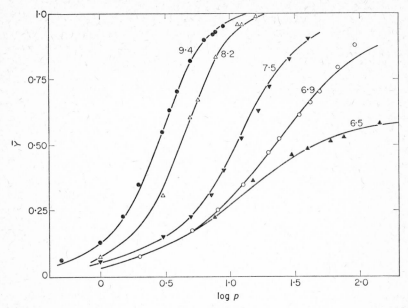

FIGURE 2. Oxygen dissociation curves of haemoglobin from *Thunnus thynnus* at 20° in tris-(hydroxymethyl)aminomethane buffers, ionic strength 0·1. Haemoglobin concentration: 4–5 mg/ml (Rossi Fanelli and Antonini, 1960).

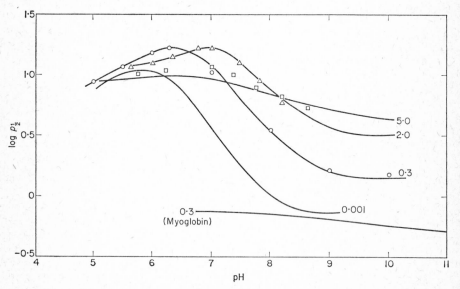

FIGURE 3. Effect of ionic strength (NaCl) on the Bohr effect for human haemoglobin (3–5 mg/ml) at 20°. The curves are from direct observations while the points indicated are from differential titrations (see text). Curves for human and horse myoglobin are shown for comparison (Antonini *et al.*, 1962, 1963a).

line side it increases up to pH 9, where it reaches a limiting value approximately 10 times the minimum; on the acid side it also increases, but to a lesser extent—this constitutes the so-called reverse Bohr effect (Antonini *et al.*, 1962). Horse haemoglobin is remarkably similar to human haemoglobin; both show very nearly the same Bohr effect and in both the shape of the oxygen equilibrium curve is essentially the same and independent of pH (Figure 1).

Other haemoglobins, especially non-mammalian ones, may be different, as for example, those of tuna fish (Rossi Fanelli and Antonini, 1960) and lamprey (Antonini *et al.*, 1964b). In the case of tuna fish haemoglobin, the shape of the oxygen equilibrium curve changes greatly with pH, as shown by Figure 2. In lamprey haemoglobin the shape of the oxygen equilibrium curve is, as in the mammalian haemoglobins, essentially independent of pH; on the other hand the Bohr effect curve has a different form and position from that of human or horse haemoglobin, being very steep and occupying a more acid pH range (Figure 1).

LINKAGE RELATIONS

Thermodynamically the oxygen Bohr effect is a linkage phenomenon between oxygen-combining sites and ionizing groups (Wyman, 1948). The change in oxygen affinity with pH is one aspect of it; the other, the converse aspect, is the change in proton affinity with oxygen saturation (or oxygen pressure). The two aspects are interrelated by the following fundamental equation

$$\left(\frac{\partial \log p}{\partial \mathrm{pH}}\right)_Y = \left(\frac{\partial \bar{H}^+}{\partial Y}\right)_{\mathrm{pH}} \tag{1}$$

where p is oxygen pressure, $\bar{H}^+$ is protons bound per haem, and Y is fractional saturation with oxygen. By introducing the concept of median oxygen pressure p_m, explained elsewhere (Wyman, 1964), this may be replaced by the more convenient relation

$$\left(\frac{d \log p_m}{d \mathrm{pH}}\right) = \Delta \bar{H}^+ \tag{2}$$

where $\Delta \bar{H}^+$ is the difference in protons bound per haem between oxygenated and deoxygenated haemoglobin. It is to be emphasized that equation (2) is of general validity, provided only the system is at equilibrium, and holds even when the molecule dissociates or undergoes any other kind of reaction (Wyman, 1964). When the ligand equilibrium curve (Y versus $\log p$) is symmetrical p_m is the same as $p_{\frac{1}{2}}$. When the curve is not symmetrical but invariant in shape changes of pH, p_m may still be identified with $p_{\frac{1}{2}}$ in equation (2).

In our experiments the Bohr effect has been studied in both its aspects, that is, the change in ligand affinity with pH and the change in the base bound by haemoglobin resulting from combination with ligand. The oxygen equilibrium was measured by a spectrophotometric method (Rossi Fanelli and Antonini, 1958) with dilute haemoglobin solutions (about 5 mg/ml) in phosphate, acetate and borate buffers generally at an ionic strength of 0·3–0·5. The difference in base bound by Hb and HbO₂ (or HbCO) was determined by measuring the pH change in an unbuffered haemoglobin solution, containing appropriate amounts of NaCl, resulting from combination of haemoglobin with the ligand (Antonini *et al.*, 1963a). From the pH changes and from the titration curves of HbO₂ (or HbCO) obtained

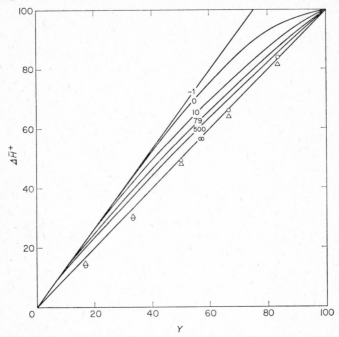

FIGURE 4. Values of $\Delta \overline{H}^+$, expressed as percentage of total, versus fractional saturation Y of Hb with CO, calculated from smooth curves of linearity experiments in 0·3 M NaCl. ○, data at pH 7·88 (final); △, data at pH 6·97 (final). The curves shown for comparison were reckoned for a model in which proton binding is the same for each of the first three steps of the reaction but zero for the fourth. The first three constants are supposed to have their statistical values, but the fourth (K_4) to be different. The numbers associated with each curve give the parameter $\alpha = (K_4/K_{4\text{stat}} - 1)$, where $K_{4\text{stat}}$ is the statistical value of K_4; α therefore represents the relative excess of K_4 over its statistical value. This model was suggested by a recent analysis of the oxygen equilibrium by Roughton.

under the same conditions, the difference in base bound, at constant pH, by the different haemoglobin derivatives was easily calculated.

In order to compare the Bohr effect as measured by the change in ligand activity with that given by the difference in protons bound, values of $\log p_{\frac{1}{2}}$ as a function of pH were calculated, according to equation (2), by graphical integration of the experimental curves of $\Delta \overline{H}^+$ versus pH.

Figure 3 shows that the directly measured values of $\log p_{\frac{1}{2}}$ agree with those calculated in this way from the observed values of $\Delta \overline{H}^+$ within the experimental error. This provides a check on the consistency of the results and *also* shows that changes in the binding of other ions during oxygenation is negligible in comparison with that of protons.

BOHR EFFECT FOR DIFFERENT LIGANDS

The Bohr effect for the reaction of human haemoglobin with carbon monoxide is very similar to that with oxygen. The total difference in protons bound by Hb and HbCO is the same as for Hb and HbO$_2$ at every pH studied (Antonini *et al.*, 1963a). Also, for both oxygen and carbon monoxide the difference in protons bound is proportional to the fractional saturation with ligand (Antonini *et al.*, 1963a). In the case of oxygen this linearity can be deduced from the invariance in shape of the equilibrium curve with pH. For carbon monoxide, for which extensive data on the shape of the equilibrium curve at different pHs are lacking (Joels and Pugh, 1958), the linearity between the fractional saturation and the proton uptake has been verified directly at low and high ionic strengths as shown in Figure 4. This provides

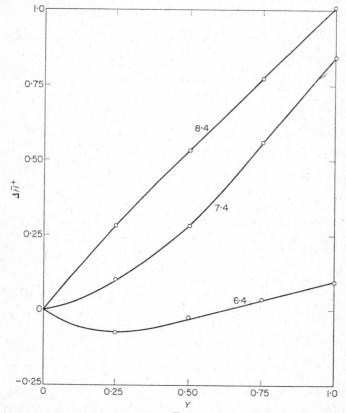

FIGURE 5. Difference in proton binding ($\Delta \bar{H}^+$) between human deoxyhaemoglobin and ferrihaemoglobin versus fractional oxidation (Y) at different pH values and 25°.

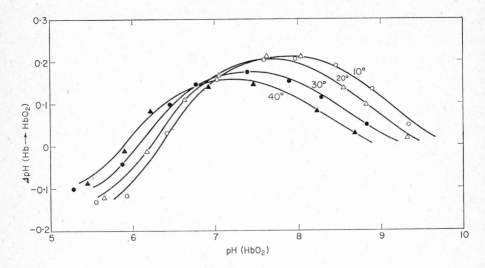

FIGURE 6. pH difference between (human) Hb and HbO$_2$ versus pH of HbO$_2$ at various temperatures. Symbols are: $\bigcirc$, 10°; $\triangle$, 20°; $\bullet$, 30°; $\blacktriangle$, 40°C.

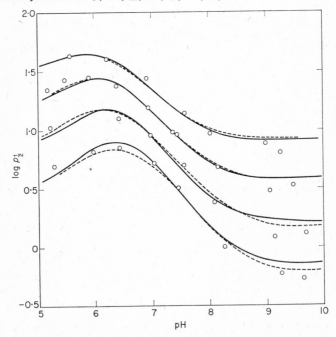

FIGURE 7. Comparison of directly observed values of log $p_{\frac{1}{2}}$ ($\bigcirc$) with those calculated from differential titrations (dashed curves) at different temperatures, i.e. 10°, 20°, 30°, 40°C going from the bottom to the top of the figure. Solid lines are calculated curves assuming the two oxygen linked acid groups (see text).

strong evidence for the validity of the original Haldane laws (Douglas *et al.*, 1912).

The Bohr effect for the oxidation–reduction equilibrium of human haemoglobin is different from that for oxygen. Even after allowance for the ionization of the water molecule occupying the sixth co-ordination position of the iron atom in ferrihaemoglobin (pK $\sim$ 8·0) it is greater, and the change in proton bound is *not* proportional to the fractional oxidation. As a result of the latter fact the shape of the equilibrium curve is grossly dependent on pH (Antonini *et al.*, 1964d). These findings are illustrated in Figure 5.

EFFECT OF SALTS ON THE BOHR EFFECT

The oxygen Bohr effect changes greatly with salt concentration (Antonini *et al.*, 1962, 1963a). It decreases with increasing ionic strength and tends to vanish at $\Gamma/2 \sim 5$ (Figure 3). Analysis in terms of two oxygen linked acid groups indicates that this is mainly due to the influence of the salt on the pK values of the groups in *oxyhaemoglobin*. In deoxyhaemoglobin the values remain about the same but in oxyhaemoglobin they change with the ionic strength, so that the difference between the two tends to decrease. The large decrease in the Bohr effect in concentrated salts may partly be ascribed to the screening effect of salts on electrostatic interactions which are presumably involved in the pK change of the oxygen linked groups.

BOHR EFFECT IN MODIFIED HAEMOGLOBINS

The oxygen Bohr effect in human haemoglobin changes as a result of a variety of modifications of the molecule as shown in Table I. It may be seen that, generally speaking, a reduction in the Bohr effect accompanies a reduction or loss in the haem–haem interactions and an increase in the oxygen affinity; however there are exceptions. Thus in HbCPA the haem–haem interactions are completely eliminated although the Bohr effect is reduced by no more than 70%. In HbCPB the haem–haem interactions remain intact, but the Bohr effect is reduced to the same extent as in HbCPA. In most cases the normal and reverse Bohr effects are modified, if at all, by about the same amount. However, in cystine treated haemoglobin there is a *reduction* of the normal Bohr effect and an increase in the reverse Bohr effect.

The Bohr effect and other interactions of the various ligand binding sites of haemoglobin (and indeed allosteric effects in proteins generally, of which these phenomena are the prototypes) have been interpreted in terms of conformational changes. In accordance with this interpretation the influence of most of the different modifications shown in Table I would represent conformational effects.

EFFECT OF TEMPERATURE ON THE BOHR EFFECT

Some years ago an attempt was made to identify the groups responsible for the Bohr effect by determining their heat of ionization (Wyman, 1939b). This was done by making differential titration curves at different tempera-

TABLE I. Changes in Oxygen Equilibria of Variously Modified Haemoglobins

Compound	Treatment or modification	n in Hill equation	O$_2$ affinity (1/$p_{\frac{1}{2}}$ at pH 7)	Bohr effect (Total change in log $p_{\frac{1}{2}}$)	References
Normal human Hb	At ionic strength 0·3	2·9	log $p_{\frac{1}{2}}$ 1·05	1·1	Antonini et al. (1962)
Normal human Hb	In 5 M NaCl	3·0	Nearly normal	Decreased to about ⅓ normal	Antonini et al. (1962); Antonini et al. (1963a); Rossi Fanelli et al. (1961)
Normal human Hb	In 6 M urea	1·3	10× increase	Absent	Rossi Fanelli et al. (1959a); Kaziro and Tsushima (1961)
Reconstituted proto-Hb	Globin + protohaem	2·7	Normal	Normal	Rossi Fanelli and Antonini (1959a)
Reconstituted deutero-Hb	Globin + deuterohaem	1·7	1·5-2× increase	Normal	Rossi Fanelli and Antonini (1959b)
Reconstituted meso-Hb	Globin + mesohaem	1·6	5-6× increase	Normal	Rossi Fanelli et al. (1959b)
Reconstituted haemato-Hb	Globin + haematin	1·0	2-3× increase	—	Antonini et al. (1964a)
Haemoglobin H	Naturally occurring abnormal haemoglobin β_4	1·0	30× increase	Absent	Benesch et al. (1961)
PMB-Hb	p-Chloromercuribenzoate (0·5-1·0 moles/Fe)	1·5	Nearly normal	Nearly normal	Benesch and Benesch (1961); Riggs (1952)

TABLE I.—*continued*

NEM-Hb	N-Ethyl maleimide (0·5–1·0 moles/Fe)	2·0	2× increase	Decreased to about ½ normal	Benesch and Benesch (1961); Riggs (1961)
IAM-Hb	Iodoacetamide (0·5–1·0 moles/Fe)	2·0	2× increase	Nearly normal	Benesch and Benesch (1961); Riggs (1961)
Cystine-Hb	Excess Cys, pH 9 Excess then removed	2·8	2× increase	Nearly normal	Taylor et al. (1963)
Acetylated-Hb	Excess acetic anhydride	1·3–2·5	10× increase	Nearly absent	Bucci et al. (1963)
Guanidinated-Hb	1-Guanyl-3,5-dimethyl Pyrazole nitrate	2·0	2× increase	Normal	R. Zito and E. Antonini (unpublished)
Fluorescein-Hb	Fluorescein isothiocyanate	1·2	5× increase	Nearly absent	Antonini et al. (1964c)
Bromthymol blue-Hb	Bromthymol blue	2·9	Normal	Decreased to about ½ normal	Antonini et al. (1963b)
Hb-CPA	Carboxypeptidase A digestion	1·0	30× increase	Decreased to about ½ normal	Antonini et al. (1961)
Hb-CPB	Carboxypeptidase B digestion	2·7	10× increase	Decreased to about ½ normal	Antonini et al. (1961)
Hb-CPA + B	Carboxypeptidase A+B digestion	1·0	50× increase	Absent	Antonini et al. (1961)

tures. It appeared that the effect of changing the temperature was simply to displace the curves along the pH axis without altering their shape. This would imply that the heat of ionization of all the oxygen linked groups is the same, and that it is also the same in oxygenated and deoxygenated haemoglobin; in addition the Bohr effect curves are invariant for changes of temperature and the inherent heat of oxygenation is independent of pH (i.e. the total observed heat based on measurements at constant pH corrected for the heat of accompanying ionization of the oxygen linked groups). From the pH displacement of the differential titration curves produced by changing the temperature it was estimated that the heat of ionization of all the oxygen linked acid groups, both those responsible for the normal and the reversed Bohr effect, was between 6000 and 7000 cal, a value characteristic of imidazole. This is the same as the apparent heat of ionization in the middle pH range of oxyhaemoglobin as a whole. By making use of this value the inherent heat of oxygenation was estimated as $13,500 \pm 500$ cal. These measurements were made with horse haemoglobin.

Recently, Rossi, Chipperfield, and Roughton (1963) studied the titration curves of human haemoglobin as a function of temperature between the pH range 7–8. They obtained a value for the apparent heat of ionization of oxyhaemoglobin of 6000–7000 cal, but a consistently higher value, higher by nearly 1000 cal, for the deoxygenated derivative. However, they failed to find such a difference in horse haemoglobin. This effect in human haemoglobin was attributed by them to a real difference in the inherent heat of ionization of the oxygen linked acid groups in oxy- and deoxyhaemoglobin. This interpretation would mean that the Bohr effect curves could not be invariant in shape for changes of temperature and that the inherent heat of oxygenation would vary largely with pH.

In view of this, we have made a systematic study of the Bohr effect in human and horse haemoglobin, measuring both the oxygen equilibrium and the differential titration curves as a function of temperature between pH 5·5 and 9·5. We have also redetermined the apparent heat of ionization of the oxygenated form. The results for human haemoglobin are shown in Figures 6 and 7. They accord in a general way with the more limited observations of Rossi, Chipperfield and Roughton, but in the light of the larger body of data now available we suggest an alternative interpretation as follows. There are two oxygen linked acid groups per haem; in human haemoglobin, as in horse, one of these, the more alkaline one, accounts for the normal, the other for the reversed Bohr effects according to the original model. The more alkaline group has a heat of ionization of 8000–10,000 cal, the same in both oxy- and deoxyhaemoglobins; the other has a much lower heat of ionization. Owing to this difference the mean pK's of the two groups move together as the temperature rises and their overlapping increases. Since the two groups affect $\log p_{\frac{1}{2}}$ in opposite ways; the result is a flattening of the Bohr effect curves at higher temperatures and serves to explain the other observed phenomenon. The inherent heat of oxygenation is independent of pH and has a value of about 14,000 cal in human haemoglobin. This interpretation is consistent with the original view that the more alkaline of the oxygen linked acid groups is imidazole although an α-amino group cannot be definitely excluded; it suggests that the other group, responsible for the reversed Bohr effect, might be a carboxyl group.

CONCLUSIONS

It has generally been assumed, ever since the original analysis of Wyman (1939a, b) that there are just two oxygen linked acid groups per haem in both human and horse haemoglobin, one of which (the more acid one) is weakened, the other strengthened, as a result of oxygenation. On the basis of the effect of temperature on the Bohr effect it was deduced that both these groups were imidazole, with a heat of ionization of about 6500 cal, the same in oxy- and deoxyhaemoglobin. Owing to the linkage of these groups with oxygen it was originally supposed that one of them served as the point of attachment of the haem to the globin and that the other was at least nearby. Although it has now been established that in horse haemoglobin histidine is indeed the residue to which the haem is attached (Perutz et al., 1960), the old argument no longer holds. Some time after the original analysis it was suggested that it is by no means necessary to suppose that the groups responsible for the Bohr effect are attached, or are even in close proximity, to the oxygen binding sites (Wyman and Allen, 1951). If the effect is due to conformational changes involving the molecule as a whole these groups might well be far from the sites where the changes are initiated. After all, in myoglobin, in which histidine is also the point of attachment of the haem, there is virtually no Bohr effect at all, and here there is evidence that oxygenation involves no major conformational change such as has now been established for haemoglobin.

The results described in this paper strengthen the argument that the group responsible for the normal Bohr effect in human haemoglobin is an imidazole; they also suggest that the group responsible for the reverse Bohr effect, may perhaps be a carboxyl group. The idea that the Bohr effect involves just two oxygen linked imidazoles should not be taken as gospel. Indeed, the possibility that more than two groups per haem may be in some degree implicated in the effect cannot be ruled out. Moreover, it is possible that these acid groups may themselves interact. Alberty has suggested an explanation in terms of negative interactions in horse haemoglobin (Alberty, 1955). In the case of lamprey haemoglobin the extreme steepness of the Bohr effect curve would seem to demand positive interactions (Antonini et al., 1964b). Still another complication which cannot be ignored is that the oxygen linked acid groups may not be the same in the α and the β chains. One should of course look for the simplest explanation of the phenomena, but as more and more precise measurements become possible one should be ready to reappraise and reformulate the hypothetical model. It is, naturally, the nature of the model which is of interest, rather than numerical details, but new facts, even apparently minor numerical revisions, may call for drastic modifications of kind.

REFERENCES

Alberty, R. A. (1955). *J. Amer. chem. Soc.* **77**, 4522.

Antonini, E., Wyman, J., Zito, R., Rossi Fanelli, A. and Caputo, A. (1961). *J. biol. Chem.* **236**, PC60.

Antonini, E., Wyman, J., Rossi Fanelli, A. and Caputo, A. (1962). *J. biol. Chem.* **237**, 2773.

Antonini, E., Wyman, J., Brunori, M., Bucci, E., Fronticelli, C. and Rossi Fanelli, A. (1963a). *J. biol. Chem.* **238**, 9.

Antonini, E., Wyman, J., Moretti, R. and Rossi Fanelli, A. (1963b). *Biochim. biophys. Acta* **71**, 124.

Antonini, A., Brunori, M., Chiancone, E., Caputo, A., Rossi Fanelli, A. and Wyman, J. (1964a). *Biochim. biophys. Acta* **79**, 284.

Antonini, E., Wyman, J., Bellelli, L., Siniscalco, M. and Rumen, N. (1964b). *Arch. Biochem. Biophys.* **105**, 404.

Antonini, E., Wyman, J., Brunori, M. and Chiancone, E. (1964c). *Biochim. biophys. Acta* **82**, 355.

Antonini, E., Wyman, J., Brunori, M., Taylor, J. F., Rossi Fanelli, A. and Caputo, A. (1964d). *J. biol. Chem.* (in press).

Benesch, R. and Benesch, R. E. (1961). *J. biol. Chem.* **236**, 405.

Benesch, R. E., Ranney, H. M., Benesch, R. and Smith, G. W. (1961). *J. biol. Chem.* **236**, 2927.

Bohr, C., Hasselbalch, N. and Krogh, A. (1904). *Scand. Arch. Physiol.* **16**, 402.

Bucci, E., Fronticelli, C., Bellelli, L., Antonini, E., Wyman, J. and Rossi Fanelli, A. (1963). *Arch. Biochem. Biophys.* **100**, 364.

Douglas, C. G., Haldane, J. S. and Haldane, J. B. S. (1912). *J. Physiol.* **44**, 275.

Joels, N. and Pugh, L. G. C. E. (1958). *J. Physiol.* **142**, 63.

Kaziro, K. and Tsushima, K. (1961). In "Haematin Enzymes", ed. by J. E. Falk, R. Lemberg and R. K. Morton. Pergamon Press, London.

Perutz, M. F., Rossmann, M. G., Cullis, A. F., Muirhead, H., Will, G. and North, A. C. T. (1960). *Nature, Lond.* **185**, 416.

Riggs, A. (1952). *J. gen. Physiol.* **36**, 1.

Riggs, A. (1961). *J. biol. Chem.* **236**, 1948.

Rossi, L., Chipperfield, J. R. and Roughton, F. J. W. (1963). *Biochem. J.* **87**, 33P.

Rossi Fanelli, A. and Antonini, E. (1958). *Arch. Biochem. Biophys.* **77**, 478.

Rossi Fanelli, A. and Antonini, E. (1959a). *Arch. Biochem. Biophys.* **80**, 299.

Rossi Fanelli, A. and Antonini, E. (1959b). *Arch. Biochem. Biophys.* **80**, 308.

Rossi Fanelli, A. and Antonini, E. (1960). *Nature, Lond.* **186**, 895.

Rossi Fanelli, A., Antonini, E. and Caputo, A. (1959a). *Arch. Biochem. Biophys.* **85**, 2.

Rossi Fanelli, A., Antonini, E. and Caputo, A. (1959b). *Arch. Biochem. Biophys.* **85**, 37.

Rossi Fanelli, A., Antonini, E. and Caputo, A. (1961). *J. biol. Chem.* **236**, 397.

Rossi Fanelli, A., Antonini, E. and Caputo, A. (1964). *Advanc. Protein Chem.* **19**, 73.

Taylor, J. F., Antonini, E. and Wyman, J. (1963). *J. biol. Chem.* **238**, 8.

Wyman, J. (1939a). *J. biol. Chem.* **127**, 1.

Wyman, J. (1939b). *J. biol. Chem.* **127**, 581.

Wyman, J. (1948). *Advanc. Protein Chem.* **4**, 407.

Wyman, J. (1964). *Advanc. Protein Chem.* **19**, 222.

Wyman, J. and Allen, D. W. (1951). *J. Polymer Sci.* **7**, 499.

DISCUSSION

H.-D. OHLENBUSCH (Institute of Physiological Chemistry, Kiel, Germany): Regarding the relationship between imidazole and a carbonyl group in horse-Hb pointed out by Antonini, I should like to remark that we found a similar phenomenon in studying the reversible denaturation of horse ferrihaemoglobin in the acid region. This is a monomolecular reaction with respect to haemoglobin. The dependence on pH suggests that there are triggering groups which must bind protons, as Steinhardt found years ago. From the effect of altering the ionic strength we conclude that four or more groups per polypeptide chain of haemoglobin are trigger groups. Their apparent pK value lies between 2 and 2·5, which suggests that we are dealing with carboxyl groups.

On the other hand, during the reaction additional protons are bound to the molecule, as Steinhardt has also found. There is strong evidence that these groups are imidazole. We have recently published work which indicates that the apparent pK of these groups in the *native* haemoglobin lies between 3·5 and 4·0. We suppose that the shift of the pK value of the imidazole group is caused by hydrogen bonds in the native molecule. (These experiments have been performed together with P. Schulte.)

H. N. FERNLEY and P. G. WALKER: We have been interested in conformational changes associated with the affinity of an enzyme for its substrate (Fernley and Walker, 1964); it seems that Dr. Perutz's paper provides evidence for a possible link between the Bohr effect with haemoglobin and a conformational equilibrium. The effect of pH on the affinity of haemoglobin for oxygen can be treated as a two-stage process, firstly a pH-dependent equilibrium between "loose" and "tight" conformations, and secondly a pH-independent association of oxygen with the "tight" conformation. Tanford (1961) has pointed out that a pH-dependent conformational equilibrium necessarily involves differences in the titration curves of the two forms and this is precisely what is found with haemoglobin. A tightening in conformation may be expected to "bury" some dissociable groups, in each case favouring the uncharged form. Hence tightening should (1) increase the pK of a carboxyl group and (2) decrease the pK of an amino or imidazole group. Antonini *et al.* (1962)† concluded from a study of pH and temperature effects that a carboxyl group and an amino or imidazole group are thus implicated in the Bohr effect. These results show that the affinity of haemoglobin for oxygen may be controlled by a conformational equilibrium which is itself dependent on the pH of the medium.

REFERENCES

Antonini, E., Wyman, J., Rossi Fanelli, A. and Caputo, A. (1962). *J. biol. Chem.* **237**, 2773.

Fernley, H. N. and Walker, P. G. (1964). Abstr. 1st Meeting Fed. European Biochem. Soc. A104.

Tanford, C. (1961). *J. Amer. chem. Soc.* **82**, 1628.

† Antonini *et al.*: "The Oxygen Linked Acid Groups in Haemoglobin". See p. 143.

Studies on the Dissociation of Human Haemoglobin†

By G. Guidotti

Biological Laboratories, Harvard University, Cambridge, Massachusetts, U.S.A.

One form of the molecule of normal adult human carbonmonoxyhaemoglobin (CO haemoglobin) is a tetramer, composed of 2α and 2β polypeptide chains. The chains are held together in the $\alpha_2\beta_2$ molecule by non-covalent bonds, whose integrity depends on the pH, ionic strength, and the dielectric constant of the solvent (for review, see Guidotti *et al.*, 1963).

In recent reports (Guidotti and Craig, 1963; Guidotti *et al.*, 1963), we have presented evidence that the dissociation may be described by the reactions:

$$\alpha_2\beta_2 \overset{K_1}{\rightleftarrows} 2\alpha\beta \overset{K_2}{\rightleftarrows} 2\alpha + 2\beta$$

and that normal adult human CO haemoglobin is a solute in rapid association–dissociation equilibrium under all solvent conditions. These conclusions are in agreement with the earlier proposal of Vinograd and Hutchinson (1960) and with the experimental data of Drabkin and Wise (1962).

The experiments to be described here were done to obtain further proof for the scheme shown above, and to obtain values, albeit approximate, for the dissociation constants, K_1 and K_2.

MATERIALS AND METHODS

The CO haemoglobin was prepared from freshly drawn blood (G.G.) and used within 10 days of its preparation (Hill *et al.*, 1962). The preparation and characterization of CO haemoglobin derivatives in which cysteine residues 93β have reacted with N-ethylmaleimide (NEM) and iodoacetamide (INH$_2$) have been described (Guidotti and Konigsberg, 1964). The membrane diffusion was carried out as previously described (Guidotti and Craig, 1963). Sephadex chromatography was done on G-200 gel in a 4×50 cm column, as described by Flodin (1961). The buffer for elution was 0·2 M NaCl, 0·001 M sodium phosphate, pH 7. All the samples were applied to the column in a volume of 5 ml and elution was carried out at 23°C at a rate of 25 ml/hr. Fractions of 8 ml were collected and analysed by determining the absorbance at 418 mμ and 540 mμ on a Zeiss PMQII spectrophotometer.

RESULTS

In a previous communication (Guidotti *et al.*, 1963) we showed that *chemically produced* mixtures of CO haemoglobins with different chromatographic

† Supported in part by a grant (National Science Foundation GB 1255) to Professor John T. Edsall.

157

properties separate into pure components during the chromatographic procedure. It was assumed that during the chemical reactions (alkylation of the
sulphydryl group of cysteine residues 93β with NEM and INH_2) molecules
of the type $\alpha_2 \beta^+ \beta^*$ would be formed in a statistical ratio (β^+ and β^* refer to
the NEM- and INH_2-derivatives of the β chain, respectively). With this
assumption, it was argued that the experiment proved the existence of the
rapidly established equilibrium $\alpha_2 \beta_2 \rightleftarrows 2\alpha\beta$ at neutral pH.

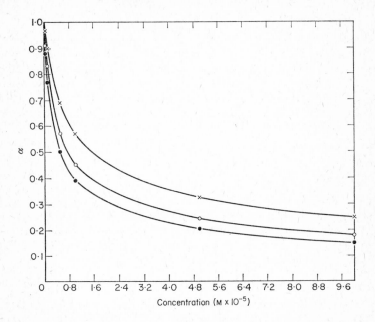

FIGURE 1. The relationship between the fraction (α) of dimer and the total concentration
of CO haemoglobin (C) for the reaction:

$$\begin{array}{cc} & K \\ \alpha_2\beta_2 & \rightleftarrows 2\alpha\beta \\ C(1-\alpha) & 2\alpha C \end{array}$$

K is the dissociation constant and has a value of 10^{-5} M. ●—● single species; ○—○,
equimolar mixture of three interacting species; ×—×, equimolar mixture of three non-
interacting species.

It is also apparent that, if this equilibrium exists, mechanical admixture of
originally pure haemoglobin species should produce hybrid molecules.
Figure 1 shows the theoretical relationship between the total concentration
of CO haemoglobin and the fraction of CO haemoglobin in the form of
dimers, assuming that the equilibria involve only tetramers and dimers. The
lower curve is for a single pure species ($\alpha_2 \beta_2 \overset{K}{\rightleftarrows} 2\alpha\beta$; $K = 10^{-5}$ M). The
middle curve would be obtained with an equimolar mixture of three different

haemoglobins which inter-react to form all the possibly hybrid molecules ($K = 10^{-5}$ M for all reactions):

$$\alpha_2\beta_2 \rightleftarrows 2\alpha\beta \qquad \alpha_2\beta\beta^+ \rightleftarrows \alpha\beta + \alpha\beta^+$$
$$\alpha_2\beta_2^+ \rightleftarrows 2\alpha\beta^+ \qquad \alpha_2\beta\beta^* \rightleftarrows \alpha\beta + \alpha\beta^*$$
$$\alpha_2\beta_2^* \rightleftarrows 2\alpha\beta^* \qquad \alpha_2\beta^+\beta^* \rightleftarrows \alpha\beta^+ + \alpha\beta^*$$

The upper curve is for an equimolar mixture of three haemoglobins, which do not interact. The system here behaves as if the overall dissociation constant had a value of $3K$ (3×10^{-5} M), where K is the constant for each pure species.

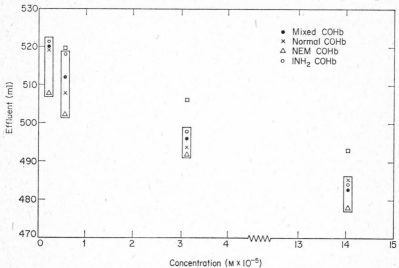

FIGURE 2. The concentration dependence of the elution positions of CO haemoglobins from Sephadex G-200. Symbols in the rectangles are experimental points. The mixed COHb is an equimolar mixture of the other three pure species. The small squares represent the calculated elution position for a mixture of non-interacting species.

If the three pure haemoglobins do not have the same values for the dissociation constants, then an interacting mixture of the three species will behave as if the overall dissociation constant had a value which is the average of those for all the reactions written above. In any case, it would always have a value smaller than that for the overall constant for a similar mixture of non-interacting species. Furthermore, during zone or boundary separation processes, the shape of the boundary should be symmetrical for the interacting system and asymmetrical for the non-interacting system in which the pure species have different values for the dissociation constants.

Figure 2 shows the results obtained with Sephadex chromatography of normal, NEM-reacted, and INH$_2$-reacted CO haemoglobins, and with an equimolar mixture of the three CO haemoglobins. The elution position of the peak is plotted against the initial CO haemoglobin concentration. As would be expected for a dissociating system, the solute is retained in the gel to a greater extent the more dilute its concentration.

It appears that the INH_2-reacted and the NEM-reacted CO haemoglobins have a slightly greater and smaller tendency to dissociate, respectively, than does normal CO haemoglobin. The dissociation curve for the equimolar mixture of the three haemoglobins, which lies between those for the pure species, indicates that there is interaction between all the subunits. The expected position for the curve if there were no interaction is shown by the small squares.

Figure 3 shows the chromatographic patterns obtained with two co-centrations of normal CO haemoglobin (panel A) and of the equimolar

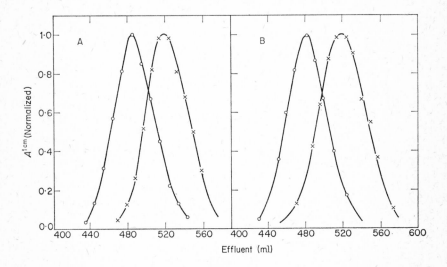

FIGURE 3. Chromatography on Sephadex G-200 of normal CO haemoglobin (A) and an equimolar mixture of normal, NEM-reacted, and INH_2-reacted CO haemoglobins (B). Initial CO haemoglobin concentration: $\bigcirc$—$\bigcirc$, 14×10^{-5} M; $\times$—$\times$, 0.2×10^{-5} M.

mixture of CO haemoglobins (panel B). The peaks are quite symmetrical in both cases, and similar except for a slight broadening of the peak for the mixed haemoglobins at low concentration (panel B, peak 2).

These data indicate that hybrid molecules do in fact exist and support our previous conclusion about the mechanism of dissociation. Preliminary experiments on the rates of diffusion of these mixtures support these data.

Winzor and Scheraga (1963, 1964) have studied other interacting systems by Sephadex chromatography, and have done detailed analyses of their data. I have preferred to interpret the present data on haemoglobin in a qualitative fashion. However, it is possible to interpret the dissociation data obtained

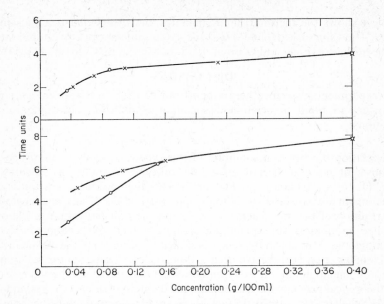

FIGURE 4. The concentration dependence of the half escape times during membrane diffusion for normal CO haemoglobin in solvents of moderate ionic strength: pH 4·70 (upper panel), pH 7·15 (lower panel). Temperature: —×—×—, 5°C; —O—O—, 25°C. The time units are: 1 hr for the experiments at 25°C; and 2·1 hr for the experiments at 5°C.

by thin film dialysis in a quantitative fashion. Figure 4 shows the relationship between the half escape time and the initial solute concentration for CO haemoglobin in a solvent of pH 7·15 (lower panel) and pH 4·70 (upper panel). In each panel, the crosses indicate the experiments performed at 5° and the circles those at 25°. With the aid of several assumptions (Guidotti, 1963) it is possible to calculate values for the constants K_1 and K_2 which are necessarily of limited accuracy but probably represent the correct orders of magnitude.

TABLE I. Thermodynamic Data for the Association of Human CO Haemoglobin at 25°C

pH		K(1/mole)	ΔG(kcal/ mole)	ΔH(kcal/ mole)	ΔS (e.u.)
7·15	Step 1	10^5	− 6·9	0 (± 2)	+ 23 (± 6)
(0·2 M Sodium phosphate)	Step 2	10^6	− 8·2	− 10 (± 4)	− 7 (± 13)
4·70	Step 1	10^4	− 5·5	0 (± 2)	+ 18 (± 6)
(0·2 M Sodium acetate)	Step 2	5×10^5	− 7·8	0 (± 2)	+ 26 (± 6)

Step 1. $\alpha_2 \beta_2 \rightleftarrows 2\alpha\beta.$ Step 2. $\alpha\beta \rightleftarrows \alpha + \beta.$

Table I shows the thermodynamic data for the *association* reactions indicated. The values for ΔG and ΔH at pH 4·7 are in agreement with the results in the literature (Field and O'Brien, 1955; Hasserodt and Vinograd, 1959).

DISCUSSION

The experiments described here support our conclusion that haemoglobin is a system in rapid association–dissociation equilibrium according to the reactions:

$$\alpha_2\beta_2 \rightleftarrows 2\alpha\beta \rightleftarrows 2\alpha + 2\beta$$

The relationship between equilibria of this type and the reaction of haemoglobin with gases has been discussed several times over the past 50 years. In fact, Douglas, Haldane, and Haldane (1912) first proposed a sequence of reactions involving the dissociation of polymeric units of aquohaemoglobin, the reaction of the monomers with gas, and the polymerization of the oxygenated monomers to explain the sigmoid-shaped oxygenation curve of haemoglobin. More recently, schemes similar in principle to the one described by Douglas *et al.* (1912) have been demonstrated to describe the reaction of lamprey haemoglobin with oxygen (Briehl, 1963), and have been suggested on theoretical grounds for mammalian haemoglobin (Briehl, 1963; Guidotti, 1963; Schejter *et al.*, 1963). In fact, there are certain anomalous phenomena with regard to the oxygenation of human haemoglobin which seem almost impossible to resolve without assuming a mobile equilibrium between the subunits of the haemoglobin molecule (persistence of values in the Hill equation near 3 when the haemoglobin is largely dissociated into units with only 2 haems (Rossi Fanelli *et al.*, 1961; Antonini *et al.*, 1962).

However, the schemes suggested so far, which may be described by the reactions:

$$A_n \rightleftarrows nA$$
$$A + O_2 \rightleftarrows AO_2$$
$$nAO_2 \rightleftarrows A_n(O_2)_n$$

fail to consider the mechanism of dissociation.

On the basis of the present data, I suggest that (1) the reaction of haemoglobin with ligands may involve the subunits (either monomers or dimers) as the reactive species, and (2) that all possible hybrid molecules are involved in the overall equilibrium of haemoglobin with ligands.

The latter point means that the reaction between ligand and haemoglobin involves 16 different equilibria if the monomers are involved, and 14 if the dimers are involved. These relationships may be condensed into one equation which relates the activity of ligand for the total activity of reacted and unreacted haemoglobin by all the various equilibrium constants (see Appendix).

It is certainly possible to relate the observed oxygenation curve of haemoglobin to these equations. However, the validity of these relationships will require that values for the various equilibrium constants be experimentally determined and tested in these equations. I am at present working along these lines with both normal and chemically altered haemoglobins.

ACKNOWLEDGMENTS

This work was done partly in the laboratory of Professor Lyman C. Craig of the Rockefeller Institute, New York, New York, and in large part in that of Professor John T. Edsall of the Biological Laboratories, Harvard University. To both Professors Craig and Edsall, I am grateful for their advice, criticisms, and hospitality.

REFERENCES

Antonini, E., Wyman, J., Rossi Fanelli, A. and Caputo, A. (1962). *J. biol. Chem.* **237**, 2773.

Briehl, R. W. (1963). *J. biol. Chem.* **238**, 2361.

Douglas, C. G., Haldane, J. S. and Haldane, J. B. S. (1912). *J. Physiol.* **44**, 275.

Drabkin, D. L. and Wise, C. D. (1962). *J. biol. Chem.* **237**, PC 261.

Field, E. O. and O'Brien, J. R. P. (1955). *Biochem. J.* **60**, 656.

Flodin, P. (1961). *J. Chromatogr.* **5**, 103.

Frieden, C. (1963). *J. biol. Chem.* **238**, 3286.

Guidotti, G. (1963). Ph.D. Dissertation, The Rockefeller Institute.

Guidotti, G. and Craig, L. C. (1963). *Proc. nat. Acad. Sci., Wash.* **50**, 46.

Guidotti, G. and Konigsberg, W. (1964). *J. biol. Chem.* **239**, 1474.

Guidotti, G., Konigsberg, W. and Craig, L. C. (1963). *Proc. nat. Acad. Sci., Wash.* **50**, 774.

Hasserodt, U. and Vinograd, J. (1959). *Proc. nat. Acad. Sci., Wash.* **45**, 12.

Hill, R. J., Konigsberg, W., Guidotti, G. and Craig, L. C. (1962). *J. biol. Chem.* **237**, 1549.

Rossi Fanelli, A., Antonini, E. and Caputo, A. (1961). *J. biol. Chem.* **236**, 397.

Schejter, A., Alden, A. D. and Glauser, S. C. (1963). *Science* **141**, 784.

Vinograd, J. and Hutchinson, W. D. (1960). *Nature, Lond.* **187**, 216.

Winzor, D. J. and Scheraga, H. A. (1963). *Biochemistry* **2**, 1263.

Winzor, D. J. and Scheraga, H. A. (1964). *J. phys. Chem.* **68**, 338.

APPENDIX

Several schemes, of various degrees of complexity, can be proposed to describe the reaction of haemoglobin with ligands in terms of the association–dissociation equilibria of the subunits.

With the scheme presented below there is a remarkable agreement between the calculated oxygenation curves and the experimental data. It is well recognized, however, that the presumed relationships between the dissociation equilibria and the combination of haemoglobin with ligands may be strictly a secondary phenomenon and not directly involved in the function of haemoglobin (Frieden, 1963).

With the major assumption that only dimers combine with ligands (the relationships for the situation in which monomers react are similar), the following reactions describe the equilibria between the dimers and ligands:

$$(1) \quad \alpha\beta + x \rightleftarrows \alpha^+\beta \quad (2) - K_a$$

$$(1) \quad \alpha\beta + x \rightleftarrows \alpha\beta^+ \quad (3) - K'_a$$

$$(2) \quad \alpha^+\beta + x \rightleftarrows \alpha^+\beta^+ \quad (4) - K_b$$

$$(3) \quad \alpha\beta^+ + x \rightleftarrows \alpha^+\beta^+ \quad (4) - K'_b$$

Here x denotes the activity of ligand (O_2 in the present case); α^+ and β^+ represent polypeptide chains whose haem groups have combined with ligand; the constants are association constants; and the species of dimer is designated by the number in parenthesis. The overall equilibrium between haemoglobin and a ligand involves, in addition to the four reactions above, 10 dissociation reactions between tetramers and dimers of the type:

$$(\alpha\beta)_i (\alpha\beta)_j \underset{}{\overset{K_{ij}}{\rightleftarrows}} (\alpha\beta)_i + (\alpha\beta)_j$$

where the i and j subscripts refer to the numbers which designate the dimers, and K_{ij} is a dissociation constant. The further assumptions are now made that (a) the dissociation of dimers to monomers may be neglected, and (b) the haem groups of each dimer are identical and independent ($K_a = K_a' = 2K_0$; $K_b = K_b' = \frac{1}{2}K_0$; K_0 is the intrinsic constant). The equilibrium between haemoglobin and oxygen is now described by:

$$K_0^2 p^2 = \frac{(\alpha^+\beta^+)}{(\alpha\beta)} \tag{I}$$

Where p is the partial pressure of oxygen. The concentrations of reacted (HbO_2) and unreacted (Hb) haemoglobin are related to $(\alpha^+\beta^+)$ and $(\alpha\beta)$ by:

$$
\begin{aligned}
(HbO_2) = (\alpha^+\beta^+)^2 &\left[\frac{1}{K_{44}} + \frac{1}{K_0 p}\left(\frac{3}{2}\frac{1}{K_{24}} + \frac{3}{2}\frac{1}{K_{34}}\right) + \right. \\
&+ \frac{1}{K_0^2 p^2}\left(\frac{1}{2K_{14}} + \frac{2}{K_{23}} + \frac{2}{K_{22}} + \frac{2}{K_{33}}\right) + \\
&\left. + \frac{1}{K_0^3 p^3}\left(\frac{1}{2K_{13}} + \frac{1}{2K_{12}}\right)\right] + (\alpha^+\beta^+)\left[\frac{1}{2} + \frac{1}{K_0 p}\right] \tag{II}
\end{aligned}
$$

$$
\begin{aligned}
(Hb) = (\alpha\beta)^2 &\left[\frac{1}{K_{11}} + K_0 p\left(\frac{3}{2K_{12}} + \frac{3}{2K_{13}}\right) + \right. \\
&+ K_0^2 p^2\left(\frac{1}{2K_{14}} + \frac{2}{K_{23}} + \frac{2}{K_{33}} + \frac{2}{K_{22}}\right) + \\
&\left. + K_0^3 p^3\left(\frac{1}{2K_{24}} + \frac{1}{2K_{34}}\right)\right] + (\alpha\beta)\left[\frac{1}{2} + K_0 p\right] \tag{III}
\end{aligned}
$$

We shall consider now the consequences of these equations in some special cases.

A. If the values of all the K_{ij}s are very large relative to the total haemoglobin concentration (a situation which corresponds to complete dissociation into dimers), then

$$(\alpha^+\beta^+) = \left[\frac{(HbO_2)}{\frac{1}{2} + \frac{1}{K_0 p}}\right] \qquad (\alpha\beta) = \left(\frac{Hb}{\frac{1}{2} + K_0 p}\right)$$

and

$$\log\frac{(HbO_2)}{(Hb)} = \log p + \log K_0 - \log\left(\frac{1 + 2K_0 p}{2 + K_0 p}\right) \tag{IV}$$

Thus, a plot of log $(HbO_2)/(Hb)$ against $\log p$ is a curve with a slope that varies as

$$\left(1 - d\log\left(\frac{1+2K_0 p}{2+K_0 p}\right)\Big/ d\log p\right)$$

B. If the values of the K_{ij}s are small compared to the total haemoglobin concentration (a situation encountered with haemoglobin under physiological conditions), then equation (1) reduces to:

$$\log\frac{(HbO_2)}{(Hb)} = \log p + \log K_0 + \log\frac{A}{B} \qquad (\ )$$

where

$$A = \left[\frac{K_0^3 p^3}{K_{44}} + K_0^2 p^2\left(\frac{3}{2K_{24}} + \frac{3}{2K_{34}}\right) + K_0 p\left(\frac{2}{K_{23}} + \frac{1}{2K_{14}} + \right.\right.$$
$$\left.\left. + \frac{2}{K_{22}} + \frac{2}{K_{33}}\right) + \left(\frac{1}{2K_{13}} + \frac{1}{2K_{12}}\right)\right]$$

and

$$B = \left[\frac{1}{K_{11}} + K_0 p\left(\frac{3}{2K_{12}} + \frac{3}{2K_{13}}\right) + K_0^2 p^2\left(\frac{1}{2K_{14}} + \frac{2}{K_{23}} + \right.\right.$$
$$\left.\left. + \frac{2}{K_{33}} + \frac{2}{K_{22}}\right) + K_0^3 p^3\left(\frac{1}{2K_{24}} + \frac{1}{2K_{34}}\right)\right]$$

A plot of log $(HbO_2)/(Hb)$ against $\log p$ is a curve whose slope depends on p and all the various K_{ij}s

$$\left(1 + \frac{d\log\dfrac{A}{B}}{d\log p}\right)$$

Thus, the value of the slope at this line and of $\log p$ at

$$y = 0\cdot 5\left(y = \frac{HbO_2}{Hb + HbO_2}\right)$$

can vary considerably by altering the values of appropriate sets of the K_{ij}s.

The important feature of equations (IV) and (V) is that the slope of the curve of log $(HbO_2)/(Hb)$ against $\log p$ is a variable in p, and thus should be expected to vary during the course of oxygenation, as is found experimentally.

C. The simplest case is the one in which hybrid molecules do not contribute to the process to any great extent. Equations (II) and (III) become:

$$(HbO_2) = (\alpha^+\beta^+)^2\frac{1}{K_{44}} + (\alpha^+\beta^+)\tfrac{1}{2} \qquad (VI)$$

$$(Hb) = (\alpha\beta)^2\frac{1}{K_{11}} + (\alpha\beta)\tfrac{1}{2} \qquad (VII)$$

which are easily soluble.

Figure 5 shows the relationship between the values of K_{11} and K_{44}, and the features of the oxygenation curves (y against log p), for an arbitrary

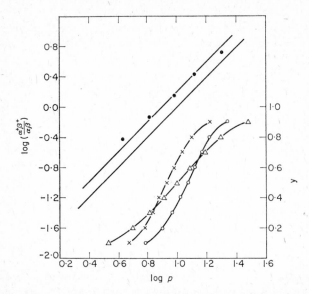

FIGURE 5. The lower straight line relates $\log(\alpha^+\beta^+)/(\alpha\beta)$ to log p according to the equations discussed in the Appendix. The sigmoid-shaped curves relating y, the fraction of reacted haemoglobin, to log p have been obtained from the straight line for a 10×10^{-5} M solution of haemoglobin and the following values for the dissociation constants: O—O, $K_{11} = 0.5 \times 10^{-5}$ M, $K_{44} = 1 \times 10^{-5}$ M; $\times$—$\times$, $K_{11} = 1 \times 10^{-5}$ M, $K_{44} = 0.5 \times 10^{-5}$ M; $\triangle$—$\triangle$, $K_{11} = K_{44} = \infty$.

The upper straight line is the curve with a slope of 2, which agrees closest with the values of $\log(\alpha^+\beta^+)/(\alpha\beta^+)$ calculated at each given log p from the data of Rossi Fanelli et al. (1961) (curve for haemoglobin in 0.25 M potassium phosphate). The values used are: $K_{44} = 1 \times 10^{-5}$ M; $K_{11} = 0.5 \times 10^{-5}$ M.

value of K_0. Clearly the slope of the curves, the p at $y = 0.5$, or both depend on the relative and absolute values of K_{11} and K_{44}.

The upper curve in the figure shows the best fit with a line with a slope of 2 for the experimental data of Rossi Fanelli et al. (1961). The values for $(\alpha^+\beta^+)$ and $(\alpha\beta)$ were calculated for the simple case without hybrid molecules. To the extent that this scheme is correct, then the deviation of the points from the straight line is indicative of the contribution of hybrid molecules to the process of oxygenation. It should be noticed that the deviations are in the direction predicted by equations (II) and (III).

The validity of this scheme or of other more complicated ones (involving monomers, or combinations of monomers, dimers, and tetramers) will rest on the ability to demonstrate the proposed equilibria.

The Subunits of Haemoglobin

E. R. HUEHNS† and E. M. SHOOTER

Department of Biochemistry, University College, London, England, and Department of Genetics, Stanford University Medical Center, Palo Alto, California, U.S.A.

Although the formation of new species in haemoglobin hybridization experiments may be most readily explained by exchange of α_2 and β_2 subunits, there are a number of phenomena, as, for example, the delay in the appearance of hybrid haemoglobins in certain systems (Robinson and Itano, 1960; Huehns and Shooter, 1961) which do not fit in with this scheme. In the alternative mechanism proposed by Vinograd and Hutchinson (1960) haemoglobin dissociates symmetrically into $\alpha\beta$ subunits, and the exchange then occurs between single α- and β-chains produced by the further dissociation of the $\alpha\beta$ subunits. If, as these authors pointed out, it is assumed that only like $\alpha\beta$ dimers may recombine, then no hybrid haemoglobins containing two unlike α- or two unlike β-chains can form, a result which agrees with the experimental observations. The failure to observe these types of hybrid haemoglobins either in red cell haemolysates or in the recombination systems has prompted the design of experiments which might be expected to lead to their formation.

One approach has utilized the recombination properties of the isolated α^A-chain subunit of haemoglobin. The α^A-chain subunit can be isolated from the eluates of Hb-A from a carboxymethylcellulose column at acid pH (Huehns *et al.*, 1962). These chains retain their haem groups. Elution of the α^A-chain preparation from Sephadex G-75 has confirmed earlier results (Huehns *et al.*, 1961) that they exist as monomer subunits. Using a borate-NaCl buffer of pH 8·3 and ionic strength 0·2, the α^A-chain subunit is eluted in a symmetrical peak ahead of the ribonuclease monomer (M.W. 12,700) but slightly behind sperm whale myoglobin (M.W. 17,800). The molecular weight calculated assuming linearity between the logarithm of the molecular weight and the ratio of effluent volume to void volume (Whitaker, 1963) is close to 16,000, which is in good agreement with the figure of 15,700 calculated from the amino acid composition. A second haem-containing component comprising 6% of the total haemoglobin of the preparation is eluted before the α^A-chain subunit as a broad zone in the range of molecular weight from 30–60,000. This fraction is reduced to 3% of the total haemoglobin if the α^A-chain zone is isolated, concentrated and analysed a second time on the Sephadex column. Such α^A-chain fractions are stable for (at least) two weeks

† Beit Memorial Fellow

at 2°C. If the α^A-chain preparation is kept at 20°C for 24 hr, however, the amount of aggregate increases to 20% of the total fraction. The fact that the α^A-chain subunit is a stable monomer at low temperatures is evidence in favour of the symmetrical dissociation of haemoglobin, the single α^A-chains originating from the dissociation of the $\alpha^A\beta^A$ subunit. In contrast to the α^A-chains, the β^A-chain or γ^F-chain subunits (the latter being formed if cord blood haemolysate is used instead of Hb-A (Dance and Huehns, 1962)) which are separated on the carboxymethylcellulose column polymerize to the tetramer state when the eluates are neutralized and have all the properties of the naturally occurring Hb-β_4^A and Hb-γ_4^F. The monomer α^A-chains combine rapidly with Hb-β_4^A at neutral pH and low temperature to form Hb-A (Huehns and Shooter, 1962). Recombination of a mixture of α^A-chains and α^G-chains (prepared from a haemolysate containing both Hb-A and the α-chain variant Hb-$G_{Bristol}$) with Hb-β_4^A leads to the possibility of forming three species, as follows:

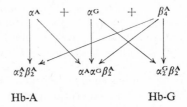

where the species with unlike α-chains, $\alpha^A\alpha^G\beta_2^A$, would have electrophoretic properties intermediate between those of Hb-A and Hb-G. However, starch gel analyses of the recombined mixture show only the zones of Hb-A and Hb-G (Shooter, Huehns and Jacobs, 1964).

Another approach makes use of the $\alpha\beta$ globin subunit and its ability to combine with haemin to reform haemoglobin (Winterhalter and Huehns, 1964). Globins A and C migrate in starch gel as single zones and have the same relative mobilities to one another as does Hb-A to Hb-C. Each globin in the presence of haemin forms the corresponding haemoglobin. The recombination of a mixture of globins A and C with haemin thus offers the possibility of testing the assumption that only like $\alpha\beta$ subunits combine. Of the three species which may form, i.e.

again, only two, in this instance Hb-A and Hb-C, were detected in the electrophoretic analysis. Thus, in both these different types of experiment a haemoglobin species with unlike α- or unlike β-chains is not observed.

Guidotti, Konigsberg and Craig (1963) have recently put forward an alternative explanation to account for the absence of these particular species. They argue that there is no specificity in the association of the $\alpha\beta$ subunits, that species with unlike α- or β-chains do form but are not detected by the usual analytical methods because of the existence at neutral pH of a rapid equilibrium between the $\alpha_2\beta_2$ tetramer and the $\alpha\beta$ subunit. On this reasoning, the third mixed haemoglobin species in both the α-chain and the globin recombination experiments described above do form but are not seen in the electrophoretic analyses.

There is, on the other hand, one exception to the rule that haemoglobins with an unlike pair of chains cannot be detected. This is Hb-F_I, a foetal haemoglobin which Schroeder, Cua, Matsuda and Fenninger (1962) have shown to have the composition $\alpha^A\gamma^F\gamma^{\text{acetyl-F}}$, where the second γ-chain is acetylated at its N-terminus. According to the equilibrium hypothesis of Guidotti et $al.$ (1963), Hb-F_I should predominantly separate into the two species $\alpha_2^A\gamma_2^F$ and $\alpha_2^A\gamma_2^{\text{acetyl-F}}$, as follows:

$$\text{Hb-}F_{II}$$

$$\alpha^A\gamma^F \;\rightleftharpoons\; \alpha_2^A\gamma_2^F$$

$$\alpha_2^A\gamma^F\gamma^{AcF} \;\rightleftharpoons\; +$$

$$\text{Hb-}F_I \qquad \alpha^A\gamma^{AcF} \;\rightleftharpoons\; \alpha_2^A\gamma_2^{AcF}$$

Hb-F_I is, however, stable when isolated and rechromatographs as a single component. There are a number of possible explanations. One is that Hb-F_I is not in equilibrium with its $\alpha^A\gamma^F$ and $\alpha^A\gamma^{AcF}$ subunits at neutral pH. This seems unlikely, for Hb-F_I forms hybrid haemoglobins at acid pH in the same way as other human haemoglobins. The alternative explanation is that the species $\alpha_2^A\gamma_2^{AcF}$ cannot form. Since hybridization experiments show that Hb-F_I does dissociate at acid pH into $\alpha^A\gamma^F$ and $\alpha^A\gamma^{AcF}$ subunits (and subsequently into single chains) it is possible to test this latter idea by dissociating Hb-F_I by exposure to pH 4·7 and then recombining the subunits in the usual way by dialysis to neutral pH. In such an experiment, one half of the Hb-F_I sample which was kept at neutral pH showed 96% of Hb-F_I when analysed on IRC 50 and 4% of a fraction which was eluted slightly ahead of Hb-F_I. After exposure of the second half of the sample to pH 4·7 (acetate buffer $I = 0·1$) for 2 hr, two new zones appeared which were identified by their chromatographic, electrophoretic and spectral properties as Hb-F_{II} and Hb-γ_4^F. However, these two accounted for only 1·5 and 1·0% of the total haemoglobin respectively, 93·5% being recovered as Hb-F_I. Thus, only one of the three possible combinations of the $\alpha^A\gamma^F$ and $\alpha^A\gamma^{AcF}$ subunit is formed in quantity, namely, the mixed species Hb-F_I ($\alpha^A\gamma^F\gamma^{AcF}$), even though one of the other combinations, Hb-F$_{II}$ ($\alpha_2^A\gamma_2^F$), is known to form readily from two $\alpha^A\gamma^F$ subunits. A plausible explanation for this result is that the third haemoglobin species, $\alpha_2^A\gamma_2^{AcF}$, cannot form. This restriction would account for the appearance of Hb-F$_I$ as a stable species, even though it is in equilibrium with its two subunits. It points also to the possible importance of N-termini of the non-α-chains in maintaining the integrity of the haemoglobin tetramer.

REFERENCES

Dance, N. and Huehns, E. R. (1962). *Biochem. J.* **83**, 40P.

Guidotti, G., Konigsberg, W. and Craig, L. C. (1963). *Proc. nat. Acad. Sci., Wash.* **50**, 774.

Huehns, E. R., Dance, N., Shooter, E. M. and Beaven, G. H. (1962). *J. mol. Biol.* **5**, 511.

Huehns, E. R. and Shooter, E. M. (1961). *J. mol. Biol.* **3**, 257.

Huehns, E. R., Shooter, E. M., Dance, N., Beaven, G. H. and Shooter, K. V. (1961). *Nature, Lond.* **192**, 1057.

Robinson, E. and Itano, H. A. (1960). *Nature, Lond.* **185**, 4712.

Schroeder, W. A., Cua, J. T., Matsuda, G. and Fenninger, W. D. (1962). *Biochim. biophys. Acta* **63**, 532.

Shooter, E. M., Huehns, E. R. and Jacobs, M. (1964). "Symposium on Cell Physiology", Springer, Berlin.

Vinograd, J. and Hutchinson, W. D. (1960). *Nature, Lond.* **187**, 216.

Winterhalter, K. H. and Huehns, E. R. (1964). *J. biol. Chem.* (in press).

Whitaker, J. R. (1963). *Analyt. Chem.* **35**, 1950.

Relations between Aggregation and Oxygen Equilibrium in Human and Lamprey Haemoglobin

R. W. BRIEHL

*Department of Physiology, Albert Einstein College of Medicine,
New York, New York, U.S.A.*

The haemoglobin of the sea lamprey *Petromyzon marinus* consists of a single polypeptide chain and haem group when it is in the oxygenated form. The oxygen equilibrium of this haemoglobin reveals three phenomena which are inconsistent with a monomeric haemoglobin: (1) n, the haem–haem interaction constant, is greater than 1 under some conditions (Wald and Riggs, 1951), (2) the oxygen affinity decreases markedly with increasing haemoglobin concentration, and (3) the magnitude of the Bohr effect depends on haemoglobin concentration. Deoxygenated lamprey haemoglobin, however, aggregates, and this aggregation is favoured by low pH and by high haemoglobin concentration. Concepts based on the relatively stable polymeric haemoglobins of mammals are not sufficient to explain the phenomena of oxygen equilibrium in lamprey haemoglobin on a number of counts: (a) n is observed to be highest at high saturations with oxygen, under which conditions the haemoglobin is monomeric, whereas n is near 1 at low saturations; (b) the concentration dependences of oxygen affinity and the Bohr effect are departures from mammalian haemoglobins, and imply intermolecular interactions.

The assumption that oxygenation of polymeric deoxyhaemoglobin takes place in two steps suffices to explain the observations (Briehl, 1963).

$$\text{Hb}_m \rightleftharpoons m\text{Hb} \tag{1}$$

$$\text{Hb} + \text{O}_2 \rightleftharpoons \text{HbO}_2 \tag{2}$$

This hypothesis implies that deaggregation must occur before oxygenation is possible. If this is so, increasing saturation decreases the concentration of the remaining deoxyhaemoglobin, causing further deaggregation and hence a greater affinity for oxygen. This increasing affinity is the phenomenon $n > 1$. If a solution of deoxyhaemoglobin is diluted, splitting will increase and affinity will rise. This is the basis of the dependence of affinity on haemoglobin concentration (the "concentration effect"). As pH is increased deoxyhaemoglobin deaggregates, and oxygen affinity therefore increases. This is the Bohr effect. Finally, at high dilution little aggregation exists at any pH, hence the magnitude of the Bohr effect decreases.

171

This hypothesis can be extended by the addition of a third reaction so that it might be applicable to tetrameric mammalian haemoglobins:

$$m\mathrm{HbO_2} \rightleftharpoons (\mathrm{HbO_2})_m \qquad\qquad (3)$$

In this form the hypothesis implies that neither oxygenation nor deoxygenation can take place until the polymeric molecule deaggregates; only an extremely small fraction need be deaggregated at a given time. It can be shown that these equilibria permit an n up to 4 for tetrameric haemoglobins. They also imply a Bohr effect if the equilibrium constants for aggregation of one or both forms of haemoglobin depend on pH. Oxygen affinity will increase as the ratio of the aggregation equilibrium constant for oxyhaemoglobin to that for deoxyhaemoglobin increases, and will decrease as the ratio decreases. Finally, if oxyhaemoglobin and deoxyhaemoglobin are both aggregated to the tetrameric state, it can be shown that there will be no concentration effect (Briehl, 1963).

Human haemoglobin deaggregates at the extremes of pH and in the presence of NaCl. Benesch, Benesch and Williamson (1962) have shown that oxyhaemoglobin splits more readily in NaCl than does deoxyhaemoglobin. We have performed oxygen equilibria, sedimentation velocity and sedimentation equilibrium studies on human haemoglobin in NaCl and at acid pH in order to determine whether the relations between aggregation and oxygen equilibrium which exist in lamprey haemoglobin are applicable to human. The sedimentation equilibria were done by the method of Yphantis (1961), and from the data molecular weights at about 0·1 mM haem and lesser concentrations can be determined. All deoxygenations were carried out with nitrogen only. For calculation of molecular weights the partial specific volume of human haemoglobin was taken as 0·748.

Figure 1 contains data from a molecular weight determination by this method. It can be seen that the molecular weight at low concentrations of haemoglobin is less than 32,000, the known weight of the dimer. It follows, therefore, that some of the haemoglobin is split to the monomeric state at pH 4·7. Guidotti and Craig (1963), have shown that deaggregation to the monomeric state also occurs in the physiological pH range in the absence of excess salt.

Figure 2 shows the molecular weights of oxyhaemoglobin and deoxyhaemoglobin in M NaCl at various pH values determined by sedimentation equilibrium. There is a pH dependence of apparent weight average molecular weight, and there is an optimum for aggregation of oxyhaemoglobin at about pH 8·8. The optimum pH for deoxyhaemoglobin is less clear, but appears to be well below that for oxyhaemoglobin. The optimum for oxyhaemoglobin occurs at a pH where oxygen affinity is high. Where affinity is at a minimum, in the range 6·0–6·5, oxyhaemoglobin splits much more readily. If the optimum pH for aggregation of deoxyhaemoglobin lies below that for oxyhaemoglobin, oxygen affinity will increase with increasing pH. This is the Bohr effect. In the lamprey the minimum affinity and the optimum

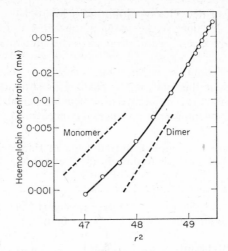

FIGURE 1. Data from sedimentation equilibrium of human oxyhaemoglobin at 2° and pH 4·7 in 0·1 M sodium acetate. Haemoglobin concentration (mM haem) is plotted against the square of the distance from the centre of rotation. Lines are drawn to indicate slopes corresponding to molecular weights of monomeric and dimeric subunits.

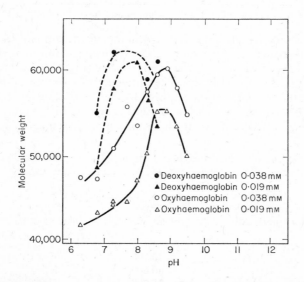

FIGURE 2. Apparent weight average molecular weights of human haemoglobin in M NaCl determined from sedimentation equilibrium. Experiments were done in 0·1 M potassium phosphate from pH 6·3–7·3, and in 0·1 M sodium borate from 7·3–9·5. All runs were at 10°. Spectra on deoxygenated samples after runs revealed less than 20% oxyhaemoglobin. Molecular weights were calculated at two places in the equilibrium distribution, corresponding to 0·019 and 0·038 mM haem.

for aggregation of deoxyhaemoglobin lie below pH 6·3. In this species the situation is simpler since oxyhaemoglobin remains a monomer.

The large difference in aggregation of oxyhaemoglobin and deoxyhaemoglobin in NaCl at pH 6·8 should produce a decreasing oxygen affinity with increasing haemoglobin concentration. Table I demonstrates such a concentration effect at this pH in 2 M NaCl. This situation parallels that for lamprey haemoglobin: a difference in molecular weight between oxyhaemoglobin and deoxyhaemoglobin produces a concentration effect.

TABLE I. Oxygen Affinity of Human Haemoglobin at Different Concentrations in the Presence and Absence of NaCl

Haemoglobin concentration (mM haem)	Oxygen tension at half saturation (mm Hg)	
	In 2 M NaCl	No added NaCl
0·06–0·10	5·34 ± 0·3	4·40 ± 0·3
0·5	6·25 ± 0·2	
10–12	6·66 ± 0·4	4·50 ± 0·3

All experiments were done in 0·1 M potassium phosphate, pH 6·8, and at 10°C.

Table II shows that at acid pH, just as in the presence of NaCl, oxyhaemoglobin deaggregates more readily than deoxyhaemoglobin. Figure 3 confirms this difference, at higher haemoglobin concentrations, by means of sedimentation velocity. Figure 4 shows the presence of a concentration effect at pH 4·7. $p_{\frac{1}{2}}$, the oxygen tension required for half saturation, rises from 0·45 mm Hg at 0·05 mM haem to 1·0 at 0·4 mM haem and higher concentrations. These findings are also similar to those for lamprey haemoglobin.

TABLE II. Molecular Weights of Human Haemoglobin at Acid pH

Haemoglobin concentration (mM haem)	Molecular weight	
	Oxy-haemoglobin	Deoxy-haemoglobin
0·056	36,700	47,000
0·047	36,600	46,300
0·038	35,000	43,000
0·028	33,900	38,600

The apparent weight average molecular weights of oxyhaemoglobin and deoxyhaemoglobin were calculated from sedimentation equilibrium at 2°C and pH 4·7 in 0·1 M sodium acetate. The deoxyhaemoglobin contained 20% oxyhaemoglobin.

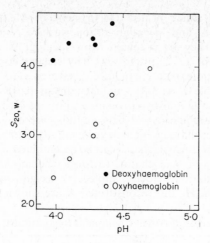

FIGURE 3. Sedimentation constants, $S_{20,w}$ of human haemoglobin at acid pH. Experiments were in 0·1 M sodium acetate. All runs were done at 2·0±0·2°C. Haemoglobin concentrations were 0·3 mM in haem.

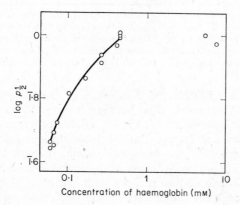

FIGURE 4. Oxygen affinity of human haemoglobin at pH 4·7. Pressure required for half saturation, $p_{\frac{1}{2}}$, is plotted against haemoglobin concentration. Experiments were performed in 0·1 M sodium acetate at 1–2°C.

Dr. Helen M. Ranney of the Department of Medicine has prepared human alpha chains, and in collaboration we have studied the properties of these subunits. They are prepared from haemoglobin A by acidification at 4°C to pH 4·7 for 12–72 hr, followed by electrophoresis at neutral pH. Under these conditions beta chains are denatured. The properties of these alpha chains resemble those of the alpha chains prepared by Huehns, Dance, Shooter and Beaven (1962) by chromatography on carboxymethylcellulose. They are largely monomeric and beta peptides are absent from the fingerprints. These chains have a high oxygen affinity with $n = 1$; there is no significant Bohr effect. Alpha chains can be recombined with haemoglobin H, which consists only of beta chains, to form reconstituted haemoglobin A. Values for sedimentation velocity, molecular weight, $p_{\frac{1}{2}}$, and n for alpha chains, haemoglobin H, and reconstituted A are shown in Table III. These

TABLE III. Properties of Alpha Chains and Reconstituted Haemoglobin A

	$S_{20,w}$	Molecular weight (M_{app})	$p_{\frac{1}{2}}$ (mm Hg)	n
Alpha chains	$2·3 \pm 0·1$	$20{,}600 \pm 2000$	$0·086 \pm 0·01$	$0·92 \pm 0·15$
Haemoglobin H			$0·044 \pm 0·01$	$1·1$
Reconstituted haemoglobin A	$4·45$		$4·4 \pm 1·5$	$1·6 \pm 0·2$
Haemoglobin A				
Electrophoretic			$3·2$	$3·01$
Fresh			$3·80 \pm 0·2$	Over $2·7$

All experiments were done in 0·1 M potassium phosphate. Sedimentation velocities were measured at about 20°C. Weight average molecular weights were determined from sedimentation equilibrium at 15–18°C. Oxygen equilibria were performed at 10°C. Oxygen equilibria for haemoglobin H and all forms of haemoglobin A were done at pH 7·0; equilibria for alpha chains were carried out at pH 6·9, 7·0 and 7·7, and showed no significant change in $p_{\frac{1}{2}}$ with pH.

oxygen equilibria reinforce the conclusion of Benesch, Ranney, Benesch and Smith (1961) that interactions between alpha and beta chains are necessary for both the Bohr effect and the low affinity of human haemoglobin A.

In both human and lamprey haemoglobin deaggregation occurs to the dimeric, and further, to the monomeric state. In both haemoglobins the deoxygenated form aggregates more strongly, and in both haemoglobins the aggregation of at least one form varies with pH in the range 6–9. In human haemoglobin under the conditions of sedimentation equilibrium, and in lamprey haemoglobin, aggregation increases with increasing haemoglobin concentration. In both species the oxygen affinity of the haemoglobin under conditions which promote or permit aggregation is low. On the other hand, conditions which maintain the monomeric state or prohibit interchain interactions are associated with high oxygen affinities and the absence of a Bohr effect. In lamprey haemoglobin the sensitivity of the aggregation of deoxyhaemoglobin to pH is the basis of the Bohr effect, and in human haemoglobin the sensitivity of the aggregation of oxyhaemoglobin and probably also of deoxyhaemoglobin is also such as to produce higher affinities at higher pHs. Thus, in the lamprey, deaggregation of deoxy-haemoglobin with increasing pH has the same effect as increasing aggrega-tion of oxyhaemoglobin does in man. Finally, in both species a concentra-tion effect is observed under certain conditions. The assumption that oxy-genation and deoxygenation take place in three steps is sufficient to explain these data and the observation $n > 1$, i.e., "haem–haem interaction". The steps are, (1) deaggregation of the deoxygenated polymer, (2) oxygenation of the deaggregated haemoglobin, (3) aggregation of the deaggregated oxy-haemoglobin; in this scheme aggregated forms cannot gain or lose oxygen. This mechanism was originally proposed by Douglas, Haldane and Haldane (1912), and they included the suggestion that deoxyhaemoglobin aggregates more strongly than oxyhaemoglobin. Their argument differed from the present hypothesis in that it assumed an appreciable proportion of oxy-haemoglobin and deoxyhaemoglobin to be deaggregated. The current hypothesis requires only that an equilibrium exist between aggregated and deaggregated forms; it is sufficient that a small but finite concentration of monomer exist. It is not excluded that a loosening of tetrameric structure occurs which is the basis of both total dissociation and the ability to gain or lose oxygen. However, even in this case, deaggregation and change of state of oxygenation are phenomena which are irrevocably linked.

REFERENCES

Benesch, R. E., Benesch, R. and Williamson, M. E. (1962). *Proc. nat. Acad. Sci., Wash.* **48**, 2071.

Benesch, R. E., Ranney, H. M., Benesch, R. and Smith, G. M. (1961). *J. biol. Chem.* **236**, 2926.

Briehl, R. W. (1963). *J. biol. Chem.* **238**, 2361.

Douglas, C. G., Haldane, J. B. S. and Haldane, J. S. (1912). *J. Physiol.* **44**, 275.

Guidotti, G. and Craig, L. C. (1963). *Proc. nat. Acad. Sci., Wash.* **50**, 47.

Huehns, E. R., Dance, E., Shooter, E. M. and Beaven, G. H. (1962). *J. mol. Biol.* **5**, 511.

Yphantis, D. A. (1961). American Chemical Society, Abstracts of Papers 140, 1C.

Wald, G. and Riggs, A. (1951). *J. gen. Physiol.* **35**, 45.

APPENDIX

If aggregation takes place only to the dimeric state, equilibria (1), (2) and (3) can be represented, respectively, by the equations

$$\frac{M_D^2}{D_D} = \frac{1}{G_D} \tag{1}$$

$$\frac{M_D}{M_O} = \frac{1}{kp} \tag{2}$$

$$\frac{M_O^2}{D_O} = \frac{1}{G_O} \tag{3}$$

M represents the concentration of monomer, D that of dimer, and the subscripts O and D refer to oxyhaemoglobin and deoxyhaemoglobin. G represents an aggregation equilibrium constant, and k an equilibrium constant for oxygenation. p is the partial pressure of oxygen. Considering the first two equilibria only, and assuming all oxyhaemoglobin is present as monomer, and almost all deoxyhaemoglobin as dimer, then $M_O = yH$, and $2D_D \cong (1 - y)H$, where y is the fractional saturation with oxygen, and H is the total haemoglobin concentration. From these equations,

$$p = \frac{y}{\sqrt{1-y}} \frac{\sqrt{2G_D}}{k} \sqrt{H}$$

Therefore, at a fixed saturation, p depends on H, i.e. there is a concentration effect. If G_D changes with pH, there will be a Bohr effect. This equation can be differentiated to give,

$$n = \frac{\partial \ln \frac{y}{1-y}}{\partial \ln p} = \frac{2}{2-y}$$

If the third equilibrium is included, and oxyhaemoglobin is mostly in the dimeric state also, then $2D_O \cong yH$ and,

$$p = \sqrt{\frac{y}{1-y}} \sqrt{\frac{G_D}{G_O}} \frac{1}{k}$$

In this situation there is no concentration effect, and $n = 2$ at all saturations. The Bohr effect depends on changes in the ratio of aggregation constants. For tetrameric haemoglobins, in the absence of partially oxygenated intermediates, the analysis is similar.

Author Index

Numbers in Italics refer to the page on which the reference is listed

Subject Index

A

Acetoacetate decarboxylase
  borohydride reduction, 118
  lysine ε-amino group in catalysis, 118
Acetylcholinesterase, amino acid sequence near active serine, 88
Activation of chymotrypsinogen, 51
Active cysteine in enzymes, 90
Active cysteine sequence
  of carboxypeptidase A, 89
  of glyceraldehyde 3-phosphate dehydrogenases, 89, 90, 99, 100
  of liver alcohol dehydrogenase, 100
  of papain, 89
  of yeast alcohol dehydrogenase, 89
Active serine in hydrolytic enzymes, 87–90
Active serine sequences
  of chymotrypsin A and trypsin, 59, 88
  of several hydrolytic enzymes, 88–89
Alcohol dehydrogenase
  horse liver
    amino acid sequence around active cysteines, 105, 106
    comparison with yeast enzyme, 106–107
    dimeric structure, 106
    formation of crystalline complexes, 137
    reaction with [1-^{14}C]iodoacetic acid, 102–103, 105
  yeast
    amino acid composition of protein subunit, 101
    amino acid sequence around active cysteines, 104, 106
    comparison with horse liver enzyme, 106–107

Alcohol dehydrogenase—yeast—*cont.*
  number of tryptic peptides, 104
  reaction with [1-^{14}C]iodoacetic acid, 102–103, 104
  tetrameric structure, 102, 104, 108
Aldolase
  activity in crystalline state, 12–13
  labelling of active centre by reduction, 118
Alkaline phosphatase, amino acid sequence near active serine, 88
Amino acid analysis, sensitivity of analytical methods, 14
Amino acid composition
  of α-chymotrypsin tryptic peptides, 48, 49
  of α-chymotrypsin B- and C-chains, 48, 49, 64
  of chymotrypsin C-chain tryptic "core", 66
  of chymotrypsinogen, 43, 45
  of the subunit of glyceraldehyde 3-phosphate dehydrogenase, 101
  of the subunit of yeast alcohol dehydrogenase, 101
Amino acid sequence, *see also* Active cysteine and Active serine
  of chymotrypsin C-chain tryptic "core", 51, 67
  A- and B-chain "histidine loops", 57
  of chymotrypsinogen A, 41, 42, 52
  of dehydrogenase lipoyl peptides, 119
  of glutamic-aspartic transaminase pyridoxyl peptide, 116
  of ribonuclease, 7
  of trypsin "histidine loop", 59
S-β-Aminoethylcysteine residues in chymotrypsin, 40
Apophosphorylase, 115
Ascorbic acid reactivation of reduced ribonuclease, 31

185